The Fantastic
Rainy Day Book

ANGELA WILKES

DORLING KINDERSLEY
London • New York • Stuttgart

A Dorling Kindersley Book

For Sam, Rose, Charlotte, Billy, Laurence, Sam, and Barney.

Designer Jane Bull
Photographer Dave King
Home Economist Jane Suthering

Project Editor Helen Drew
Text Designers Adrienne Hutchinson,
Katie Poyner, and Cheryl Telfer
Managing Editor Jane Yorke
Managing Art Editor Gillian Allan

First published in Great Britain in 1995
by Dorling Kindersley Limited
9 Henrietta Street, London WC2E 8PS

Reprinted 1995, 1996 (twice)

A CIP catalogue record for this book
is available from the British Library.

ISBN 0-7513-5256-X

Colour reproduction by Colourscan, Singapore
Printed and bound in Italy by A. Mondadori Editore, Verona

Dorling Kindersley would like to thank Chris Branfield for jacket design, Andy Crawford for additional photography, and Jonathan Buckley, Jane Horne, Jeannette Morton, Emma Patmore and Chris Scollen for their help in producing this book. Dorling Kindersley would also like to thank the following models for appearing in this book: Holly Cowgill, Kelly Gomez, Emma Judson, Laurence King, Sam Priddy, Tebedge Ricketts, Darren Singh, Selena Singh, and Phoebe Thoms.

CONTENTS

COLLECTIONS

DRESSING UP

TREATS AND PRESENTS

INTRODUCTION

This book will give you lots of inspiring ideas for things to make and do on rainy days. But before you start you must have the right materials. Here you can see lots of things used in this book. Save as many of them as you can and sort them into boxes, and they will be ready to transform into whatever you like! Remember – when you finish a project, put all your materials, equipment, and tools away in their boxes, and clean up any mess you have made.

Things to collect

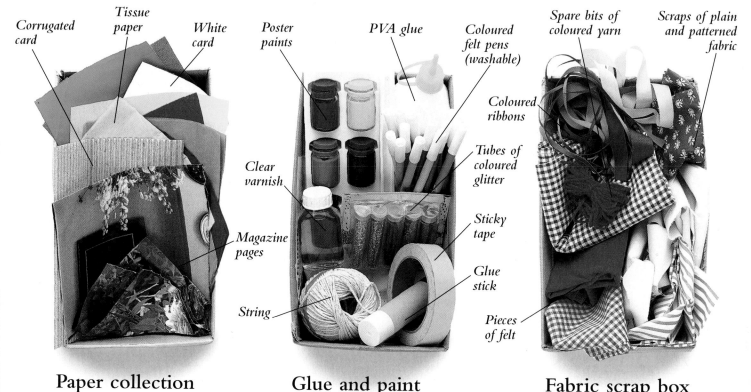

Corrugated card

Tissue paper

White card

Poster paints

PVA glue

Coloured felt pens (washable)

Clear varnish

Magazine pages

String

Coloured ribbons

Tubes of coloured glitter

Sticky tape

Glue stick

Spare bits of coloured yarn

Scraps of plain and patterned fabric

Pieces of felt

Paper collection

Save paper and card of different thicknesses, colours, and textures. The more you have the better. Keep large sheets in a tube or folder, so they don't get damaged.

Glue and paint

Here are all the different sorts of glue and paint you will need to collect to make the projects in this book. You will need strong glue and rubber-based glue, as well.

Fabric scrap box

Fabric is useful for making pictures as well as for sewing. Keep a bag of leftover fabric, yarns, and ribbons.

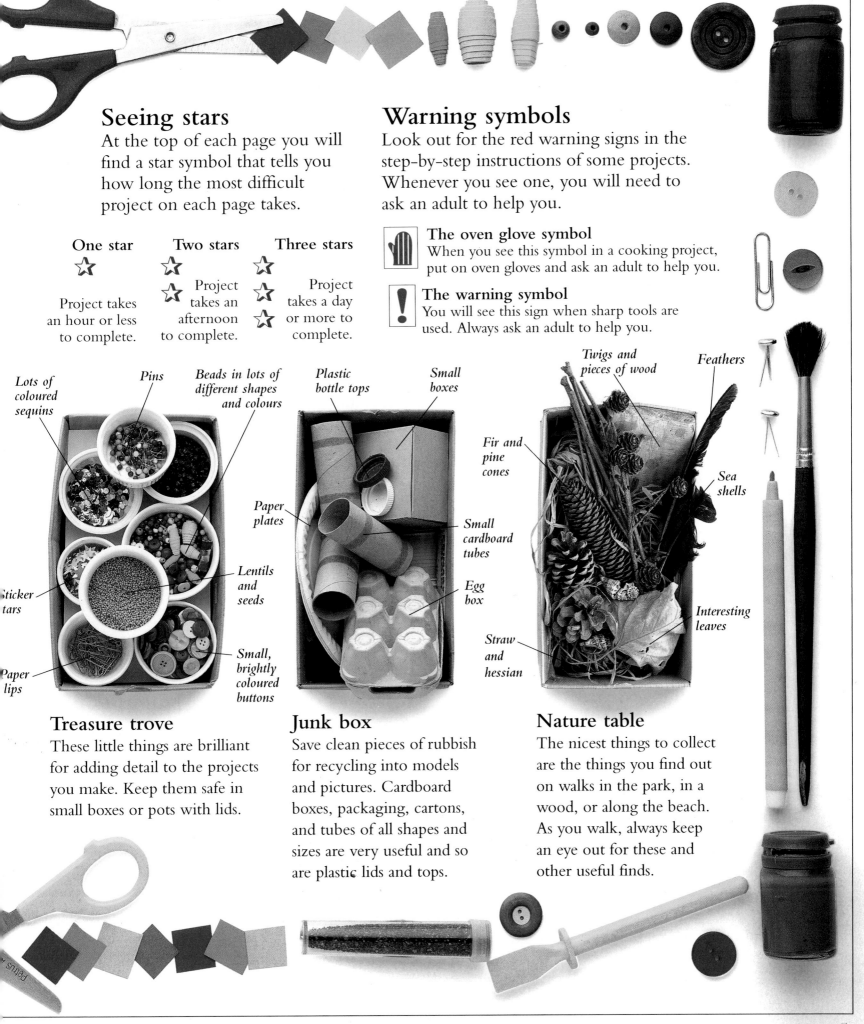

Seeing stars

At the top of each page you will find a star symbol that tells you how long the most difficult project on each page takes.

One star
☆

Project takes an hour or less to complete.

Two stars
☆
☆

Project takes an afternoon to complete.

Three stars
☆
☆
☆

Project takes a day or more to complete.

Warning symbols

Look out for the red warning signs in the step-by-step instructions of some projects. Whenever you see one, you will need to ask an adult to help you.

The oven glove symbol
When you see this symbol in a cooking project, put on oven gloves and ask an adult to help you.

The warning symbol
You will see this sign when sharp tools are used. Always ask an adult to help you.

Lots of coloured sequins

Pins

Beads in lots of different shapes and colours

Plastic bottle tops

Small boxes

Twigs and pieces of wood

Feathers

Fir and pine cones

Sea shells

Paper plates

Small cardboard tubes

Sticker stars

Lentils and seeds

Egg box

Interesting leaves

Paper clips

Small, brightly coloured buttons

Straw and hessian

Treasure trove

These little things are brilliant for adding detail to the projects you make. Keep them safe in small boxes or pots with lids.

Junk box

Save clean pieces of rubbish for recycling into models and pictures. Cardboard boxes, packaging, cartons, and tubes of all shapes and sizes are very useful and so are plastic lids and tops.

Nature table

The nicest things to collect are the things you find out on walks in the park, in a wood, or along the beach. As you walk, always keep an eye out for these and other useful finds.

MAKING PICTURES

One of the best ways to spend a rainy day is to make pictures. You don't even have to be good at drawing, as you can produce brilliant mosaics and collages from paper, seeds, pasta, magazine photographs, scraps of fabric, and glue. Below you can see how to make the different sorts of pictures. Turn the page to see the finished works of art and to find out how to frame them.

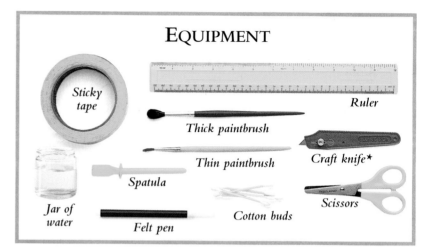

EQUIPMENT

Sticky tape

Ruler

Thick paintbrush

Thin paintbrush

Craft knife★

Spatula

Jar of water

Felt pen

Cotton buds

Scissors

You will need

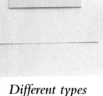

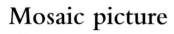

Different types of white card and paper

Scraps of fabric

Pages torn out of old magazines

Coloured paper

PVA glue with a nozzle

Dried beans, seeds and pasta

Smooth stones and pebbles

Poster paints

Clear varnish

Glue stick

Corrugated cardboard

Mosaic picture

1 Mosaics look best if you keep the shape or pattern simple. Start by drawing the outline of your picture on a piece of white card.

2 Choose the colours you want to use in your picture. Then cut pages in these colours out of magazines, and tear them into small squares.

3 Spread glue on part of the picture and stick down the squares. Start with the background and work in rows from the top downwards.

★ *Always ask an adult to help you use a craft knife.*

Paper or fabric pictures

1 Choose a piece of paper or fabric for the background, then cut it out and stick it down. Then glue strips of paper or fabric around the border.

2 Tear out paper shapes for the main image in the picture. Arrange them on the background until you are happy with the design. Glue it down.

3 Add the details to your pictures with smaller pieces of paper. Arrange the pieces on the picture before you glue them in position.

Painted pebbles

1 Choose smooth pebbles or stones. Wash them and let them dry. Next paint the pebbles all over with a thick coat of white paint and let it dry.

2 Now, paint a picture on each stone. Paint the larger areas of colour first and let them dry before painting the smaller details, with a fine brush, on top.

3 When the paint has dried, brush each pebble with clear varnish and let it dry. This helps to stop paint chipping off the stone.

Seed collage

1 Sort out lots of different coloured seeds, dried beans, and pasta. Draw an outline of your picture on a piece of white card.

2 Spread glue on part of the picture and carefully sprinkle some beans or seeds on top. Push them into place with the hard end of your paintbrush.

3 Continue sticking on seeds until the picture is finished. Add small details with lines of beans or seeds, or by breaking off small pieces of pasta.

PICTURE GALLERY

Making a frame

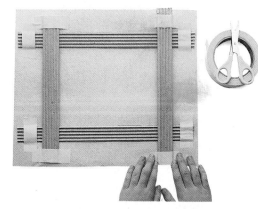

1 Cut four long strips of corrugated card each about 3 cm wide. Tape them together, on some card, to fit the size of picture you are framing.

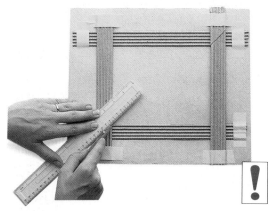

2 Ask an adult to score the edges of the card strips diagonally, as shown. Cut the strips along the score lines. Then peel off the sticky tape.

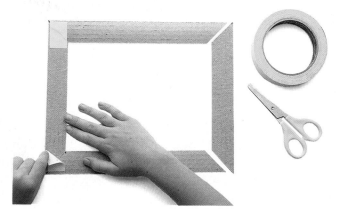

3 Turn the card over and tape the edges together. Paint and varnish the front of the frame, then tape the picture to the back of the frame.

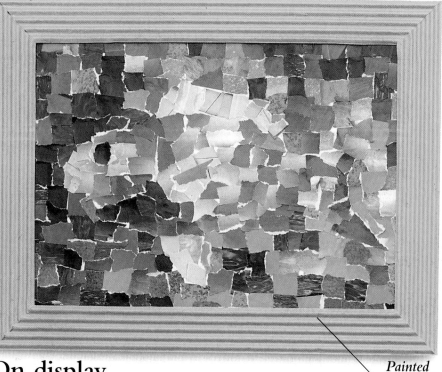

Painted corrugated card frame

On display

Here is a gallery of all the different sorts of pictures you can make. The instructions on the left show you how to make frames for your pictures, or you could mount them on a sheet of coloured paper or card, instead.

Why not make frames for your paintings, too?

Seaside painting

Fabric collage cow

Fabric fun
Make a collection of different sorts of fabric with interesting textures colours and patterns for your collages.

Tulip and bee

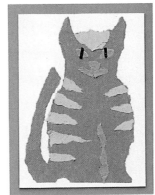

Marmalade cat

Torn paper pictures
These torn paper pictures are simple to make, and they look stunning, too. Try making cards and gift tags in the same way.

Painted beach pebbles
These pebbles have a sea-side theme. The shapes of your pebbles may suggest other ideas. The stones make fun paperweights.

Boat at sea

Beach crab

Shoal of fish

Sun and sea

Orange paper mount

Duck in the snow

Seed street collage

PAINTED FACES

You can have great fun with your friends by painting each other's faces. You can become a tiger, a clown, or anything you like! Look for pictures in books and magazines for ideas, and then copy the details when you paint. The best face paints are water-based ones, which are easy to apply and quick to wash off afterwards. You can blend face colours together to make new shades, just as you do with watercolour paints.

You will need

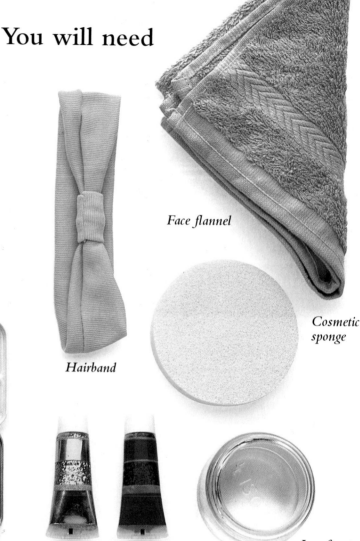

Face flannel

Hairband

Cosmetic sponge

Water-based face paints

Tubes of glitter for faces

Jar of water

Fine paintbrush

Broader, flat paintbrush

Applying a base

Put a hairband on your model. Wet the sponge and squeeze it out so it is just damp. Rub it gently in the base colour and then sponge the paint evenly over the face.

Adding the detail

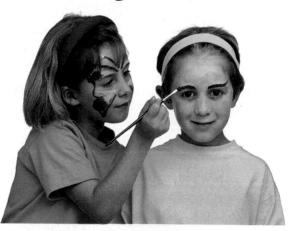

Allow the base colour to dry. Then paint on details, using the face paints like normal paints. Use the flat brush for large areas of colour and the fine brush for details.

Cleaning up

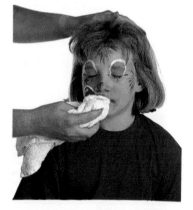

Wipe off the face paints with soap and water and a clean face flannel. Don't let soap get in the eyes.

Happy clown

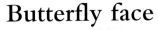

1 This face doesn't need a base. Paint two green ovals over the eyelids and eyebrows.

2 Then paint on a large, red mouth and a red circle on the end of the nose.

3 Paint white outlines round the eyes and mouth, and add white highlights where shown.

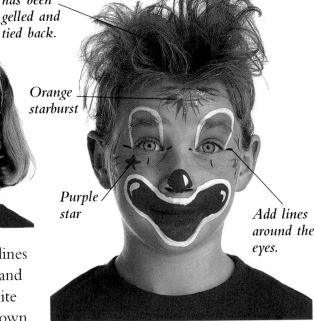

The hair has been gelled and tied back.

Orange starburst

Purple star

Add lines around the eyes.

Butterfly face

1 With the fine brush, paint on the outline of the butterfly's wings and antennae.

2 Then paint in the patches of colour inside the wing outline with the flat brush.

3 Paint smaller areas of colour with the fine brush. Add lines of glitter paint where shown.

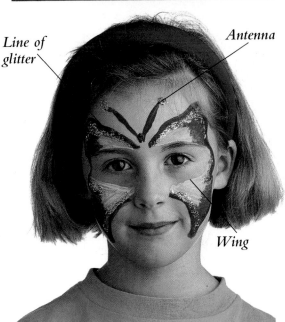

Line of glitter

Antenna

Wing

Terrible tiger

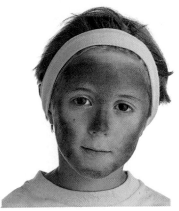

1 Sponge on yellow around the middle of the face and orange around the edges.

2 When it is dry, paint on feathery white eyes and a muzzle, and fan them out at the edges.

3 Paint a black mouth and nose. Add black lines round the eyes and spots on the muzzle.

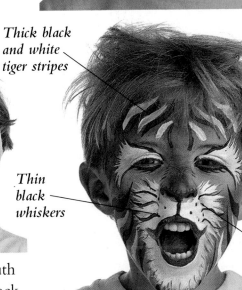

Thick black and white tiger stripes

Thin black whiskers

White fluffy muzzle

QUICK DISGUISES

With a little imagination, and bits and pieces from your scraps box, you can put together a quick disguise and turn yourself into another person. You could be a detective, a famous movie star, or even Father Christmas. Change your clothes and put on a hat and no-one will know who you really are.

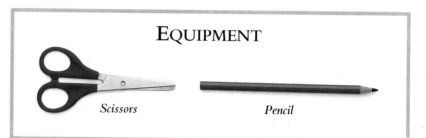

EQUIPMENT

Scissors   *Pencil*

You will need

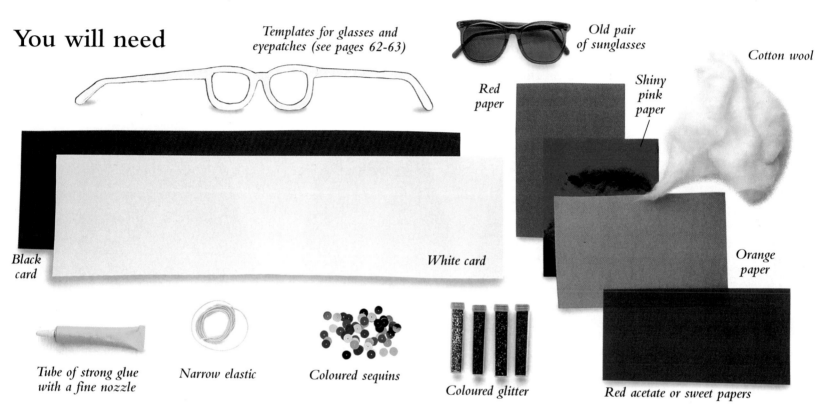

Templates for glasses and eyepatches (see pages 62-63)

Old pair of sunglasses

Cotton wool

Red paper

Shiny pink paper

Black card

White card

Orange paper

Tube of strong glue with a fine nozzle

Narrow elastic

Coloured sequins

Coloured glitter

Red acetate or sweet papers

False noses

1 Make noses out of coloured paper. Cut out a kite shape long enough to cover your nose and fold it in half. Or give the nose big, round nostrils.

2 Cut some elastic long enough to go round the back of your head. Thread it through two holes at the top of the nose and knot the ends.

Eyepatches

Using the template on page 63, draw an eyepatch on card, and cut it out. Glue on glitter, if you like. Attach a length of elastic, as for the nose.

Detective disguise

Using the template on page 62, draw and cut out glasses from black card. Glue a false nose on to the glasses and a black card moustache on to the nose.

Movie star shades

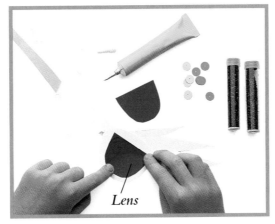

Lens

Use the glasses with wings template to make "shades". Glue lenses cut out of acetate to the back of the shades. Decorate the front with glitter.

Instant disguise

Draw a beard and moustache on white card and cut it out. Glue bits of cotton wool all over it. Tie some elastic to the sides of the moustache, as for the nose.

Disguise kit

Here are the finished disguises. They are all really quick and easy to make. You can wear each one on its own or combine two or three with a hat from page 15 for a total disguise.

False nose

Detective disguise

Wicked moustache

False nose

Old sunglasses

Instant disguise

Movie star shades

Sequin

Glitter frames

Acetate lens

Cotton wool

Pirate's eyepatch

Glittery eyepatch

Shiny false nose

Santa's beard

13

HATS GALORE

Hats come in all shapes and sizes and are great fun to dress up in. Put on a hat and you can pretend to be anyone you like. Here you can find out how to make three great hats from thin card and a few extras. You will need to measure your head with a band of card before you make the top hat and the boater.

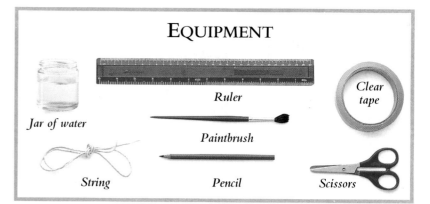
You will need

Thin black, white, and yellow card

Poster paints

Green, yellow, pink, and blue tissue paper

Green ribbon

Silky scarf

Measuring your head

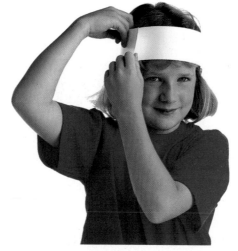

Cut a narrow strip of card and wrap it round your head. Tape down the overlapping edge. This band shows the size of your head.

2 Cut a long length of card about 16 cm tall. Roll it to fit inside the brim and tape it in place on the inside. Tape the overlapping edges.

Top hat

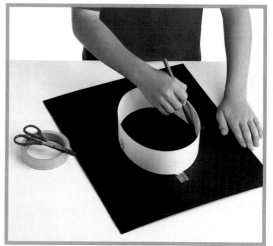

1 Tape the band to some black card. Draw round inside it. Draw a circle 5 cm out from the band. Take off the band and cut round both circles.

Boater

Make a boater 7.5 cm tall out of white card, as for the top hat. Tape the circle cut from inside the brim to the top of the hat. Then paint the hat.

Sunhat

1 To make the brim, draw one circle, as shown on page 60, 17 cm across and a second circle 42 cm across, around it. Cut out the circles.

2 Fold a sheet of tissue paper in half and gently push it into the hole, as shown. Trim off the rough edges and tape the tissue paper inside the brim.

3 Tape a scarf across the tissue paper, as shown. Scrunch squares of tissue paper into flowers and tape them around the brim of the hat.

Hat parade

And here are all the featured hats, ready to wear. Try making other styles, like a witch's hat, a crown, or even a huge sombrero to complete your dressing-up wardrobe.

Jolly boater

Hat painted with broad yellow, red, and blue stripes

Top hat

Stick a band of shiny ribbon around the hat to hide the paper join.

Tuck a colourful card under the ribbon to add a touch of colour.

Flowers made from scrunched-up tissue paper

Sunhat

Tissue paper crown

Tie the hat under your chin with the silky scarf.

Yellow card brim

15

MAKING MASKS

Why not make a mask for a fancy-dress party, for a special play, or just for dressing up? All the masks here cover your face to provide a complete disguise, and they are made from nothing more than paper plates and torn paper. Try copying the ideas shown here, or make up some masks of your own.

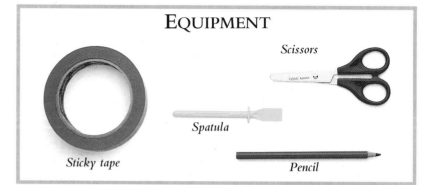

EQUIPMENT

Scissors

Spatula

Sticky tape

Pencil

You will need

Coloured paper

Large white paper plates

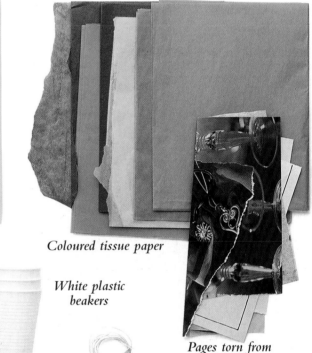

Coloured tissue paper

Rubber-based glue

Tubes of glitter

White crêpe paper

White plastic beakers

Thin elastic

Pages torn from old magazines

Red-eyed frog

Cover a plate with green and yellow tissue paper. Cut two holes for nostrils. Make the eyes from the ends of two beakers covered with tissue paper.

Harlequin mask

Tear up diamonds of pink, yellow, and blue tissue paper and glue them on to the plate. Cut two diamonds for eyes and stick on a black paper mouth.

Leo lion

Cover a plate in torn yellow and orange magazine paper. Use strips of brown tissue paper for a mane and make the features of the face out of paper.

Polar bear

Cut off the end of a beaker. Tape it into a hole the same size, cut in the centre of a plate. Then glue balls of white crêpe paper over the plate and beaker.

Bird of paradise

Make a beak from two folded triangles of yellow paper and stick them to a plate. Make a face with pink paper and glitter and feathers from tissue paper.

Adding the elastic

Make a hole at each side of the mask. Cut some elastic long enough to go round your head and thread it though the holes. Tie a knot in each end.

Red-eyed frog

Stand-out beaker eyes

Green tissue face

The nostrils are the eyeholes of the mask.

Scrunched paper mouth

Leo lion

Torn tissue paper mane

White paper whiskers

Black paper features

Polar bear

Black paper features

Ears made of card covered in pink paper and white crêpe paper balls.

Muzzle made from a paper covered beaker.

Mask collection

Here are all the finished masks. When you aren't wearing your masks, you can hang them up by the elastic on your bedroom walls.

Harlequin mask

Torn tissue diamonds

Black paper mouth

Bird of paradise

Glitter

Torn tissue crest

Blue tissue feathers

Yellow card eyes

Folded yellow card beak

MAKING SWEETS

What better way to spend a rainy afternoon than making some delicious sweets to cheer everyone up? Here, you can see everything you need to make peppermint creams, pink sugar mice, and marzipan bonbons. Then turn the page to see a mouthwatering array of the finished sweets.

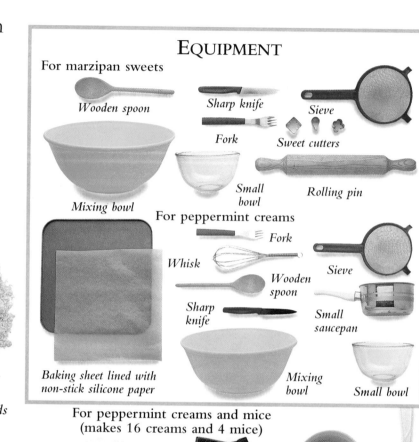

EQUIPMENT

For marzipan sweets

Wooden spoon

Sharp knife

Sieve

Fork

Sweet cutters

Mixing bowl

Small bowl

Rolling pin

For peppermint creams

Whisk

Fork

Wooden spoon

Sieve

Sharp knife

Small saucepan

Baking sheet lined with non-stick silicone paper

Mixing bowl

Small bowl

You will need

For marzipan sweets

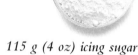

115 g (4 oz) icing sugar

225 g (8 oz) ground almonds

Pink food colouring

115 g (4 oz) caster sugar

Green food colouring

1 egg

An extra egg yolk

3 drops vanilla essence

Licorice strings

Glacé cherries

1 teaspoon lemon juice

For peppermint creams and mice
(makes 16 creams and 4 mice)

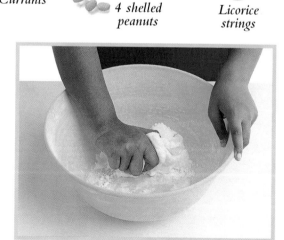

55 g (2 oz) dark chocolate

1 egg white

Pink food colouring

340 g (12 oz) icing sugar

Currants

A few drops peppermint essence

4 shelled peanuts

Licorice strings

Making the peppermint mixture

1 Put the egg white in the mixing bowl and beat it lightly with the whisk until it looks frothy but has not yet gone stiff.

2 Sift the icing sugar into the bowl. Then stir it into the beaten egg white with a wooden spoon until the mixture is stiff.

3 Add a few drops of peppermint essence and knead it into the mixture. The more essence you add, the stronger the mints will taste.

Chocolate peppermint creams

4 Split half the mixture into 16 balls and put them on the lined baking sheet. Press them flat with a fork and leave them to set for 24 hours.

5 When the creams have set, break the chocolate into the small bowl. Set the bowl over a pan of simmering water until the chocolate melts.

6 Dip each peppermint cream into the melted chocolate, then put them back on the baking sheet until the chocolate has set hard.

Sugar mice

1 Knead a few drops of pink food colouring into the other half of the peppermint mixture, then break it into four even-sized pieces.

2 Shape each piece of the pink mixture into an oval shape with your hands, then pinch one end of each oval to make a pointed snout.

3 Add two currants to each oval to make eyes and peanut halves to make ears. Cut small pieces of licorice string to make the tails.

Making the marzipan

1 Sift the icing sugar into the mixing bowl to remove any lumps. Then add the caster sugar and the ground almonds, and stir them together.

2 Mix the egg, egg yolk, lemon juice, and vanilla essence together in the small bowl. Add them to the sugar mixture and mix them in.

3 Gently knead the mixture with your hands until it becomes a smooth, thick paste. Add a little more icing sugar if the mixture is sticky.

CANDY DISPLAY

Marzipan colours

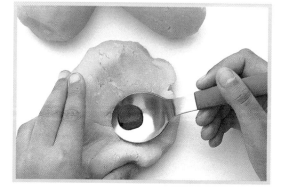

Split the marzipan into three balls. Leave one ball plain. Add a little pink colouring to one ball and green to the other. Knead until the colour is even.

Roly-poly sweets

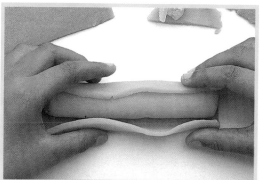

1 Roll some plain marzipan into a small sausage. Roll out the same amount of green and pink marzipan and cut each into a rectangle.

Checkerboard sweets

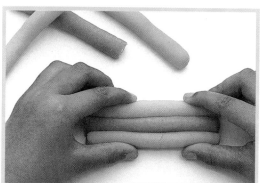

1 Cut six equal pieces of marzipan, two of each colour. Roll them into long sausages, then press three different coloured sausages together.

Cut-out sweets

Roll out some marzipan out until it is about 0.5 cm thick. Cut out shapes such as butterflies and flowers with the sweet cutters.

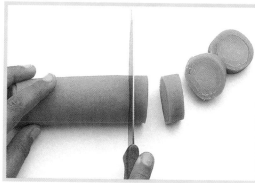

2 Roll the green and then the pink rectangles around the sausage. Then trim the ends and slice off small rounds, to make the finished sweets.

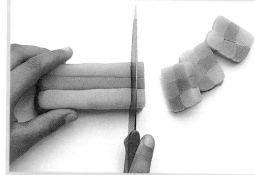

2 Press the remaining sausages on top, making sure that no sausage is next to a sausage of the same colour. Flatten the sides, and cut into slices.

Sweet treats

Arrange the finished sweets in a pretty pattern on a big plate or tray. Below is a guide to all the different types of sweets.

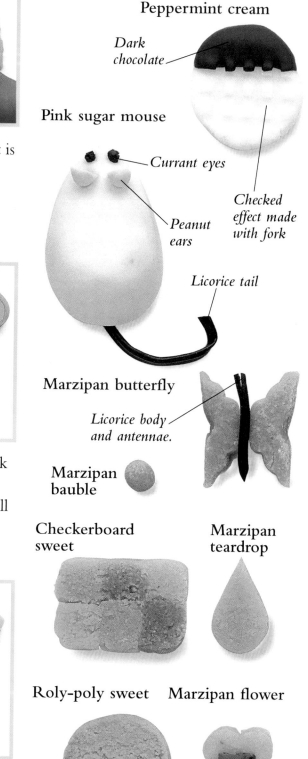

Peppermint cream

Dark chocolate

Checked effect made with fork

Pink sugar mouse

Currant eyes

Peanut ears

Licorice tail

Marzipan butterfly

Licorice body and antennae.

Marzipan bauble

Checkerboard sweet

Marzipan teardrop

Roly-poly sweet

Marzipan flower

Three rings of coloured marzipan

Piece of glacé cherry

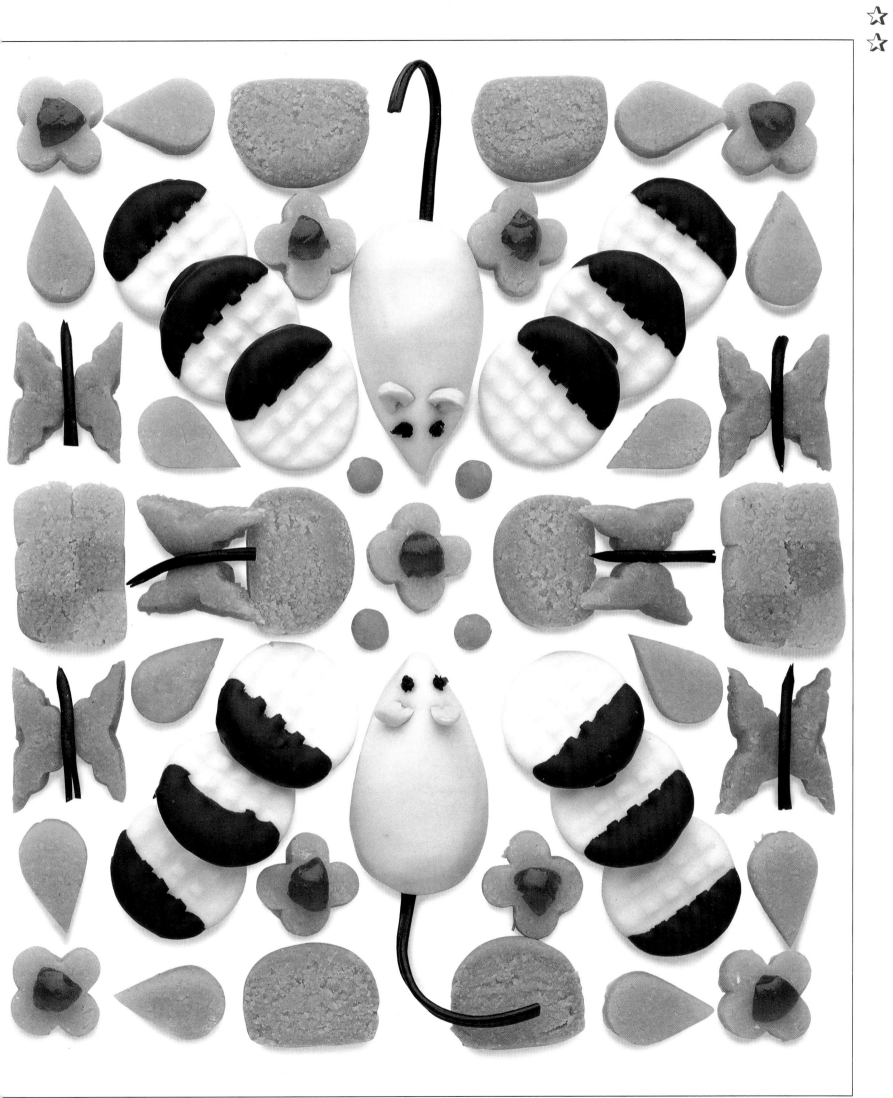

MUFFIN BONANZA

American muffins are quick to make and taste delicious still warm from the oven. Try one of the three versions shown here: white chocolate and strawberry, orange and poppyseed, or apple and cinnamon. Alternatively you could add your own ingredients to the basic recipe. The quantity given here makes 12 muffins.

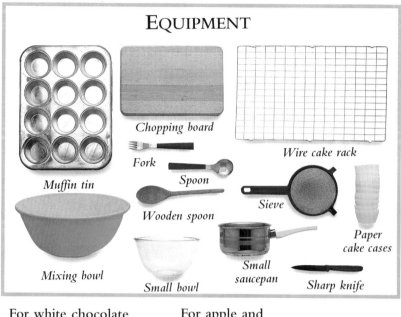

EQUIPMENT

Chopping board

Fork

Spoon

Wire cake rack

Muffin tin

Wooden spoon

Sieve

Paper cake cases

Mixing bowl

Small bowl

Small saucepan

Sharp knife

You will need

For the basic mixture

240 ml (8 fl oz) milk

85 g (3 oz) soft brown sugar

2 eggs

1 level tablespoon baking powder

A big pinch of salt

55 g (2 oz) butter

285 g (10 oz) plain flour

For white chocolate and strawberry muffins

140 g (5 oz) strawberries

55 g (2 oz) white chocolate drops

For apple and cinnamon muffins

1 dessert apple

1 teaspoon ground cinnamon

For orange and poppyseed muffins

Juice and grated rind of an orange*

1 tablespoon poppyseeds

What to do

1 Put the paper cases in the muffin tin. Set the oven to 200°C/400°F /Gas Mark 6. Melt the butter in the saucepan, then let it cool a little.

2 Sift the flour, baking powder, salt, sugar, and ground cinnamon (if using it) into the mixing bowl and stir everything together.

3 Beat the eggs in the small bowl. Pour in the milk (and orange juice if using it) and whisk it into the eggs. Then stir in the melted butter.

Replace 120 ml (4 fl oz) of the milk with the grated rind and juice of an orange.

4 Peel and chop the apple (or the strawberries) into small pieces. Add it with the rest of the ingredients and the egg mixture to the bowl of flour.

5 Beat all the ingredients together, then spoon the mixture into the muffin cases. Put them into the oven to bake for about 25 to 30 minutes.

6 The muffins are cooked when they have risen and are firm and golden brown. Move them carefully on to a wire rack to cool.

Tempting treats

Muffins taste best eaten warm from the oven, on the day they are made. However, if you have any left uneaten, put them in an airtight tin and keep it in a cool place or in the freezer. They will stay fresh for a several days.

Apple and cinnamon muffin

Orange and poppy seed muffin

Strawberry and white chocolate muffin

Pretty doily

For a special occasion decorate your plates with pretty paper doilies. Take a 30 cm square of greaseproof paper and fold it in half, twice. Then using scissors, cut a rounded edge opposite the point. Cut small shapes in the paper to make a pattern. Unfold it and you have a delicate doily.

23

JUNK JEWELLERY

You don't need gold and precious gems to make fabulous jewellery. You can create stunning necklaces, bracelets, and earrings, with paper and a few colourful bits and pieces. Look around your home for buttons, beads, shiny sweet wrappers, and ribbons, then add sequins and glitter for extra sparkle.

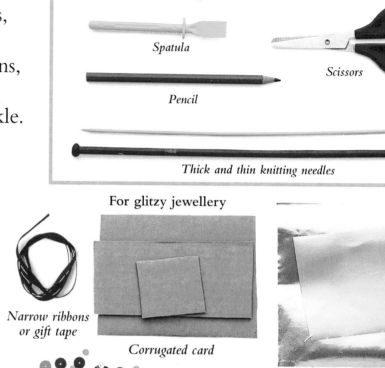

EQUIPMENT

Spatula

Scissors

Pencil

Thick and thin knitting needles

You will need

For rolled-paper jewellery

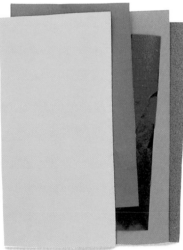

Narrow ribbons or gift tape

For glitzy jewellery

Corrugated card

Gold paper

Brightly coloured sequins

Brooch backs

Earring backs

Coloured paper in different thicknesses

Magazine pages

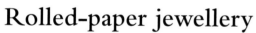
Small, wooden beads

Glue stick

PVA glue in a tube

Scraps of coloured foil and sweet papers

Rolled-paper jewellery

1 Cut out lots of long thin triangles from magazine pages and coloured paper, as shown. The triangles should be about 30 cm long.

2 Spread glue on the thinnest two thirds of each triangle. Then, starting with the wide end, roll up the triangle round a knitting needle.

3 When you have enough paper beads, thread them on to some ribbon, with a flat bead between each one, and tie the ribbon ends together.

Glitzy jewellery

1 Draw heart shapes and diamonds on corrugated card and cut them out. Cut the same shapes out of gold paper and glue them on to the card.

2 Tear up small pieces of coloured foil and sweet papers and glue them all over the gold shapes. Then glue sequins on top of the foil.

3 Make small holes in the gold shapes and thread them on to thin ribbon to make necklaces, or glue them on to earring and brooch backs.

Colourful collection

Rainbow-bright and sparkling, the finished jewellery is great fun to wear, and makes wonderful presents, too. Experiment with different shapes, designs, and colours for glitzy jewellery, and with different textures of paper for rolled-paper beads.

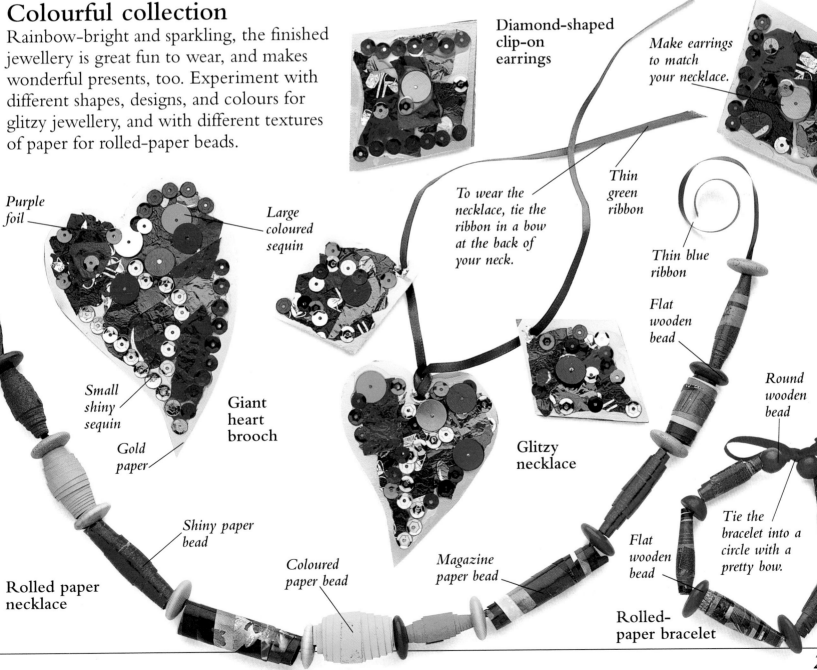

Diamond-shaped clip-on earrings

Make earrings to match your necklace.

To wear the necklace, tie the ribbon in a bow at the back of your neck.

Thin green ribbon

Thin blue ribbon

Flat wooden bead

Round wooden bead

Purple foil

Large coloured sequin

Small shiny sequin

Gold paper

Giant heart brooch

Glitzy necklace

Tie the bracelet into a circle with a pretty bow.

Flat wooden bead

Shiny paper bead

Rolled paper necklace

Coloured paper bead

Magazine paper bead

Rolled-paper bracelet

25

DOUGH MODELS

Salt dough is easy to make and can be modelled into all kinds of things. You can bake it in the oven so that it sets hard (ask an adult to help you), and then paint it bright colours. Here you can see how to make jazzy napkin rings, tiny coil pots, fabulous fishy key rings, and fun play-food badges.

You will need

200 ml (¹/₃ pint) water

1 tablespoon vegetable oil

300 g (10 oz) plain flour

300 g (10 oz) salt

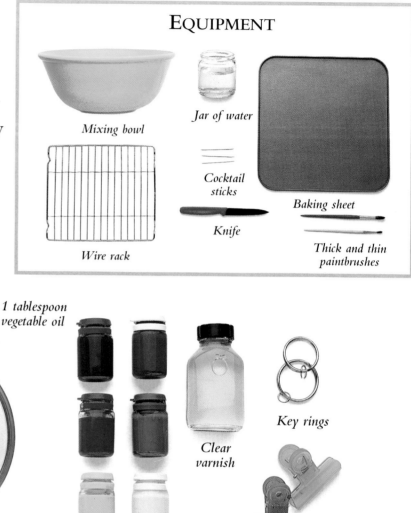

EQUIPMENT

Mixing bowl

Jar of water

Cocktail sticks

Baking sheet

Knife

Wire rack

Thick and thin paintbrushes

Clear varnish

Key rings

Poster paints

Plastic bulldog clips

What to do

1 Set the oven to 180°C/350°F/Gas Mark 4. Mix the flour, salt, oil, and water into a soft dough in the bowl. Add more water if necessary.

2 Sprinkle some flour on the table. Turn the dough on to the table and knead it with your hands, as shown, until it is smooth and stretchy.

3 Then, model the dough into the shapes you want. Stick pieces of dough together with a little water and use a cocktail stick to make small holes.

Fishy friends
You can use your models to make great presents, like fridge magnets, key rings and paper clips.

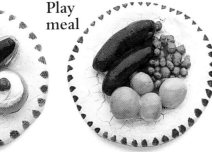

Fishy clip

4 Make a pot by coiling sausages of dough around on a circular base. Put all the dough shapes on a baking sheet and bake them for 20 minutes.

5 Let the dough shapes cool on a wire rack, then paint them in bright colours. When the paint has dried, coat them with clear varnish.

Glue a fish on to a small magnet.

Fridge magnet

Jewel bright

Here are some of the many things you can make with salt dough. Once they are painted and varnished, they will last for ever. Try making salt dough jewellery, too.

Key ring

Tie a fish to a key ring with ribbon.

Play cakes

Play meal

Play fruit

Play-food badges
Tape your mini plate on to a safety pin to make a colourful badge.

Paint your pots with colourful designs.

Mini coil pots
You can keep beads, jewellery, and other treasures in these pretty pots.

Make a personalised napkin ring for each member of your family.

Napkin rings
These colourful rings will brighten up any table. You could try making a bangle in the same way.

ALL IN A POT

You can create a beautiful garden anywhere. Flowers, herbs, and even fruit can be grown indoors in pots and window boxes. Start planting today, and watch your own garden blossom to life in front of your eyes. Turn the page for lots of interesting mini-garden ideas.

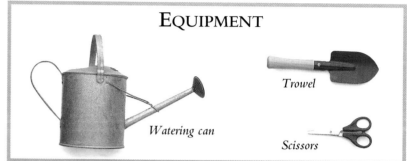

EQUIPMENT

Trowel

Watering can

Scissors

You will need

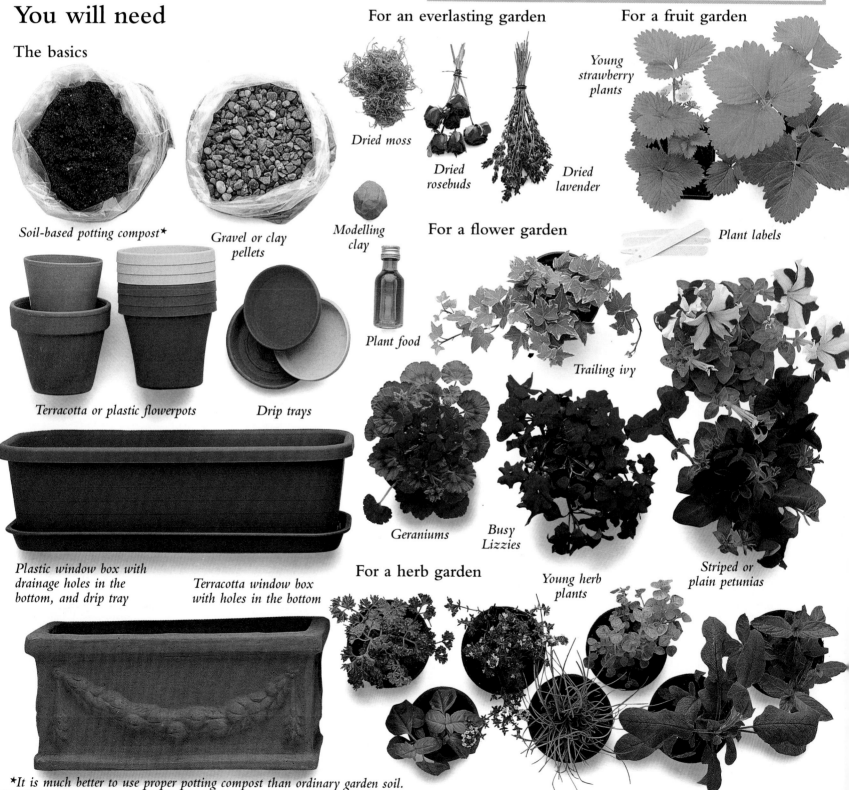

The basics

Soil-based potting compost*

Gravel or clay pellets

Terracotta or plastic flowerpots

Drip trays

Plastic window box with drainage holes in the bottom, and drip tray

Terracotta window box with holes in the bottom

For an everlasting garden

Dried moss

Dried rosebuds

Dried lavender

Modelling clay

Plant food

For a flower garden

Trailing ivy

Geraniums

Busy Lizzies

Striped or plain petunias

For a herb garden

For a fruit garden

Young strawberry plants

Plant labels

Young herb plants

*It is much better to use proper potting compost than ordinary garden soil.

Preparing for planting

1 Fill the bottom of the window box and flowerpots with a layer of gravel. This will help water to drain out of the pots better.

2 Then half-fill the window box and pots with potting compost. If the compost is very dry, water it lightly before planting anything.

Repotting a plant

Lower the plant into the flowerpot so that the bottom of its stem is just below the pot rim. Fill in the sides with compost and firm it down.

A flower garden

1 Take the plants out of their pots and decide how to arrange them. Start with the tallest plants. They look good at the back of the box.

2 Then add any low, trailing plants. It is best to put these at the front, so that they can grow down over the window box.

3 Arrange the rest of your flowers in the box. Then fill in the gaps between them with more compost and press it down firmly.

An everlasting garden

1 Break off a piece of modelling clay and press it into the bottom of a small flowerpot. This will keep the stems of the dried flowers in place.

2 Trim the stems of the dried flowers. Then start arranging them in the flowerpot by pressing them gently into the modelling clay.

3 When all the dried flowers are in place, arrange a little dried moss around the top of the pot, to make it look as if they are growing naturally.

GARDENS IN POTS

These pots and boxes of brightly-coloured flowering plants will cheer up any room or garden. Look for a sunny, sheltered spot to grow your plants, such as outside on a window ledge or inside on a wide shelf or window sill. A window box is very heavy, so you will need to ask an adult to move it.

Lavender and rose garden

Dried rose garden

Lavender garden

Terracotta flowerpot

Dried rose

Dried lavender

Moss

Everlasting flowers

These pretty dried flower gardens will never die. But they should be kept out of direct sunlight or their colours will soon fade.

Red geranium

Yellow plastic pot

Ivy

Marjoram

These ivy plants have green and white leaves.

A plant a pot

If you haven't got a window box, why not plant a group of plants in matching pots? Stand them in a row for a striking effect.

Painted pots

Try growing house plants in brightly painted pots. You can find out how to decorate flowerpots and drip trays on page 32.

This white flower will soon lose its petals, then its centre will swell and ripen to form a strawberry.

Strawberry plants

Tiny, unripe strawberry

Red petunia

Strawberry garden

Early in the summer, these strawberry plants are still in flower. If you look closely, you can see small, green strawberries forming. Before long the strawberries will grow and ripen. They are ready to pick when the berries have turned red.

Trailing ivy plant

Green plastic window box and drip tray

White plastic window box and drip tray

Herb garden

Fresh herbs look pretty sitting on a kitchen window sill and they make the kitchen smell delicious, too. It is best to trim them often, to stop the plants becoming too big. If you grow herbs outside, their flowers will attract bees and butterflies.

Chives

Golden marjoram

Purple sage

Parsley

Growing mint
Mint spreads quickly, so it is a good idea to grow it in its own pot.

Mint

Terracotta pot with drip tray

Summer garden

This colourful window box will flower all through the summer. It will need watering once a day, or more often on hot days. Removing dead flowers will make the plants flower for longer.

Thyme

Pretty terracotta window box

Red geranium

Red and white striped petunias

Purple petunia

Scarlet Busy Lizzies

Caring for your plants

1 Your pots and window boxes will need watering every day in warm weather. The compost should always feel slightly moist.

2 All plants will flower for longer and look better if you dead-head them regularly. This means snipping or picking off any dead flowers.

PERFECT POTS

Why not brighten up your house plants by painting some flowerpots to put them in? You can make plain-coloured pots, add stripes and checks, or paint on some flowers. For the best effects, keep the paint quite thick and the patterns simple. Painted pots make attractive and useful presents, too.

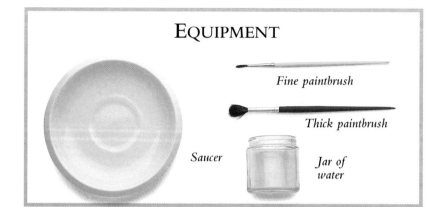

EQUIPMENT

Fine paintbrush

Thick paintbrush

Saucer

Jar of water

You will need

Clean terracotta flowerpots

Drip trays to match the pots

Poster paints

Clear, matt acrylic varnish

What to do

1 First mix the colours you want on a saucer. Use a thick brush to paint large areas of one colour, and a fine brush for patterns, like these.

2 To make patterns, paint pots in one colour and leave them to dry. Then paint stripes or checks in other colours on top of the first colour.

3 When the paint has dried, brush on a coat of clear varnish. This will make the pots waterproof and stop the paint running.

You can paint pots of all shapes and sizes. This little pot has cress growing in it.

Blue and yellow design

Plenty of pots

Here is a selection of painted pots and some of the ways you can use them, from growing houseplants and fragrant kitchen herbs, to making perfect candle holders, and a colourful desk tidy. If your pot has a drip tray, try painting it with a matching design.

Plain-coloured pot

This tiny pot makes a pretty candle holder.

Daisy design

Spotty pot design

Paint criss-cross lines for a tartan design.

Ivy

This is a herb called marjoram. Find out more about growing herbs on page 31.

Try painting the inside of the pot in a matching colour.

Stripy pot and matching drip tray

Pink tulip design

PRESSING PLANTS

Pressed flowers and leaves are beautiful and they last forever. Flowers with flat faces are the easiest to press. Choose dry, undamaged flowers and leaves and press them as quickly as you can, before they start to droop. You can stick them in a nature diary or make them into pictures and cards. Below you can find out what to do, and over the page are lots of ideas for things to make.

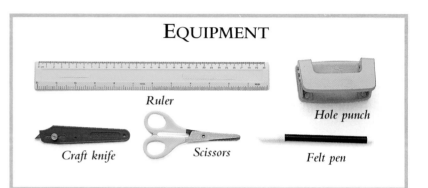

EQUIPMENT

Ruler

Hole punch

Craft knife

Scissors

Felt pen

You will need

Fresh flowers and leaves to press

A heavy book

Pansies

Geranium

Ivy leaves

Periwinkle

Welsh Poppy

Daisies

Columbine

Fern

Purple sage

Flat-faced rose

Blotting paper

Violas

Buttercup

Parsley

For the nature diary

For making pictures

Rubber based glue

Cotton buds

Corrugated card

Different sorts of paper

Tracing paper

Thin ribbon

Clear plastic film

Thick paper or thin card

Pressing flowers

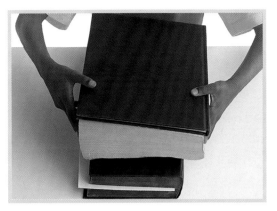

1 Open the heavy book and cut out a piece of blotting paper about the same size as the open pages. Fold the paper in half, then open it out.

2 Lay the paper on the open book. Arrange flowers and leaves flat on the right-hand side of the paper, then fold the left-hand side over the plants.

3 Press more flowers further on in the book. Then stack heavy books on top. Leave the plants to dry for at least four weeks.

Making a nature diary

1 Decide what size you want your diary to be. Then ask an adult to cut two pieces of corrugated card to make the front and back covers.

2 Cut out rectangles of paper and tracing paper just smaller than the covers to make pages. Punch holes in both pages and covers, as shown.

3 Put the paper and tracing paper inside the two covers, with the holes lined up. Tie ribbons through the holes, to hold the book together.

Making pictures

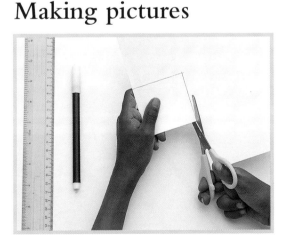

1 Cut out different-shaped pieces of white or coloured paper and card. These will be the bases for your cards, pictures, gift tags, and bookmarks.

2 Arrange the flowers and leaves on the paper or card. Then dab a tiny spot of glue on the back of each flower and gently stick it down in position.

3 To protect your cards, cut out a piece of plastic film bigger than the card. Smooth it on to the card. Stick the edges down at the back.

NATURE ON PAPER

Pressing plants is a wonderful way of keeping a picture record of all the plants you have seen growing in your garden. As well as flowers, you can press leaves, ferns, mosses, seed heads, and herbs* and keep them in a nature diary or arrange them into pictures.

Handle the pressed plants very carefully when gluing them down, as they are very fragile.

Flowers and leaves May

Herbs from the garden May

Herbal diary
You could use some pages in your diary to collect and label one type of plant, such as herbs.

Tracing paper sheet

Nature diary
Your nature diary can be a picture record of the changing seasons, with every couple of pages displaying the plants you collect each month. Even in winter you will be able to find interesting things for your diary. Put a page of tracing paper between each page of plants to stop them sticking together.

*Remember – never pick or uproot wild plants.

Flower picture

Arrange pressed flowers on a piece of paper, then mount it on a piece of card. Tape a loop of ribbon to the back so that you can hang it up. Arrange the flowers in a pretty pattern or try to make a picture with your pressed flowers and leaves.

Book mark

Use narrow strips of card to make book marks and cover the flowers with plastic film to protect them.

Nature diary's corrugated card cover

Grey paper mount

Ribbons threaded through a slit in the cover for tying the nature diary shut.

Yellow ribbon tie

Gift tags

Glue pressed flowers or leaves to a square of card. Then punch a hole in one corner of each tag and tie a ribbon through it.

Cover the tag with clear plastic film.

NATURE'S MODELS

When you are out on walks or on holiday at the seaside, keep your eyes open for interesting objects like oddly-shaped pieces of driftwood and sticks, unusual pebbles and shells, leaves, seeds, and other bits and pieces. With a little imagination, you can transform them into all kinds of models and toys. Here you can find ideas for making funny faces, wriggly snakes, boats, and a little cart. Turn the page to see what they look like.

You will need

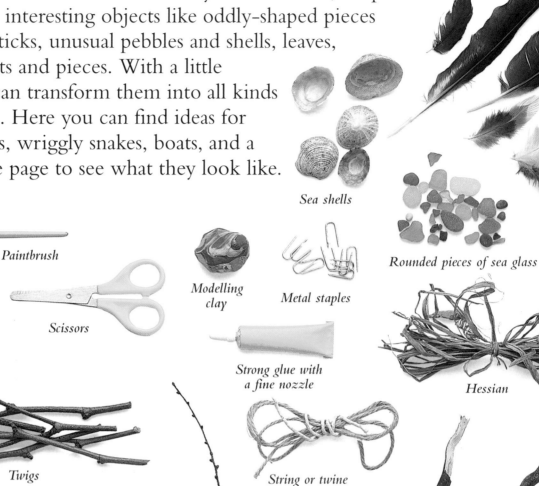

Sea shells

Feathers

Rounded pieces of sea glass

Paintbrush

Poster paints

Scissors

Modelling clay

Metal staples

Strong glue with a fine nozzle

Hessian

Twigs

String or twine

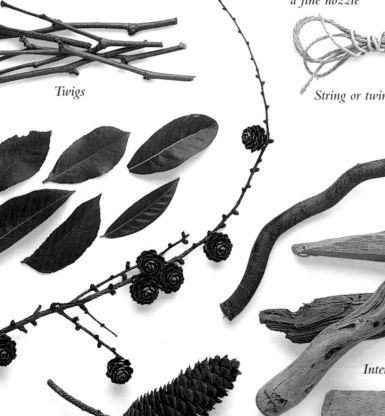

Evergreen leaves

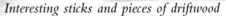

Interesting sticks and pieces of driftwood

Fir and pine cones

Funny face

Find a flat piece of wood for the face and glue small stones, cones, or shells to it, to make the features. You could use feathers or string for the hair.

Wriggly snake

Find a twisted stick and ask an adult to smooth away any rough bits. Then paint on a face and some stripes, to look like a snake's markings.

Seashell coracles

Stick small pieces of modelling clay into some shells. Thread leaves on to small sticks for the sails and push them into the modelling clay.

Jaunty clipper

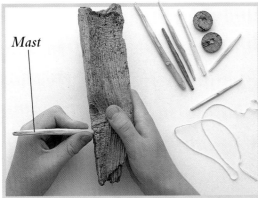

Mast

1 Ask an adult to make holes in the top of a flat piece of wood. Put sticks in the holes, for masts. Add a feather shaft to make the bowsprit.

Rigging   *Cork ring*   *Yard-arm*

Mast

Bowsprit

2 Tie small sticks to the masts to make yard-arms. Glue a ring of cork to the top of each mast. Tie string to the masts for the rigging.

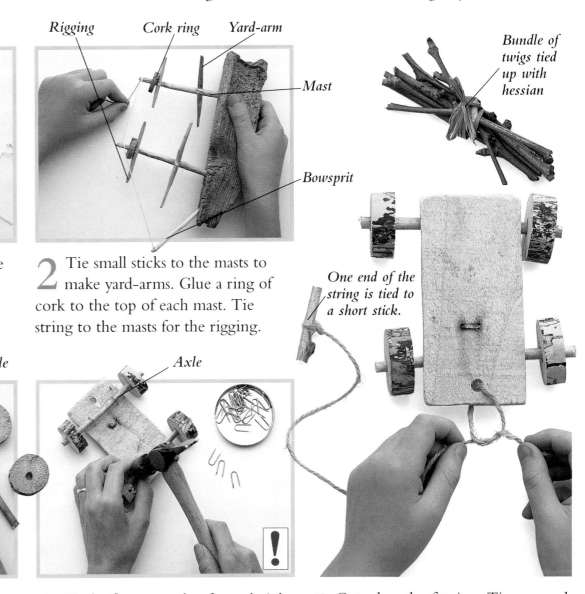

Bundle of twigs tied up with hessian

One end of the string is tied to a short stick.

Caveman's cart

Stick axle

1 To make wheels, ask an adult to saw four slices of wood from a branch and drill a hole in the middle of each. Glue them on to the ends of two sticks.

Axle

2 Find a flat rectangle of wood. Ask an adult to drill a hole in one end. Carefully nail the two axles to the wood with metal staples, as shown.

3 Cut a length of string. Tie one end to a small stick and the other to the cart. Then tie up a bundle of twigs and put it on the cart.

BEACHCOMBER'S GALLERY

Funny faces
These two faces are both stuck on to pieces of drift wood. Try out different things for the features before gluing anything down.

And here are the finished models, together with another face! Why not use them as a starting point for your ideas and design your own models. What you make will vary, depending on the natural materials you have at home.

Paper hat decorated with a feather and a twisted stick

Feather head-dress

Sea glass eyes

Shell nose

Fir cone eyes

Pebble nose

Shells for earrings

Leaf mouth

Mouth made from an old piece of cork.

Dancing lady

Chief of the forest

Shell necklace

Thick stick for arms

Wriggly snakes
Use two or three paint colours for each twisting stick snake and try to keep the pattern regular. Look at pictures of real snakes for inspiration. Paint on eyes and a mouth to add the finishing touches.

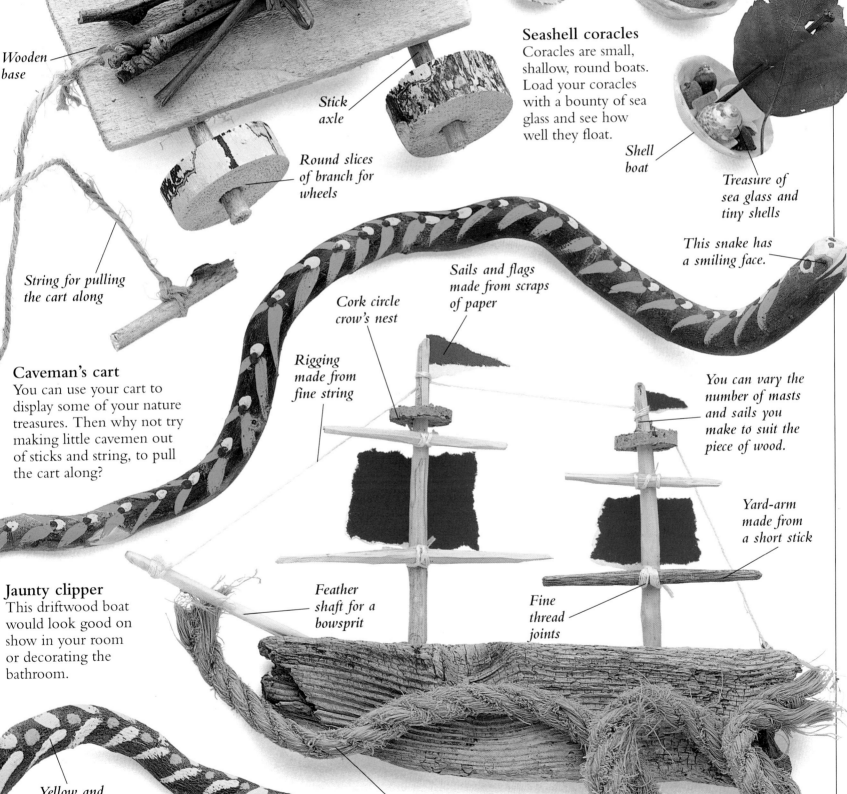

Caveman's bundle made from a collection of twigs tied with hessian

Sail made from a leaf

Twig mast

Wooden base

Stick axle

Seashell coracles
Coracles are small, shallow, round boats. Load your coracles with a bounty of sea glass and see how well they float.

Round slices of branch for wheels

Shell boat

Treasure of sea glass and tiny shells

This snake has a smiling face.

String for pulling the cart along

Sails and flags made from scraps of paper

Cork circle crow's nest

Rigging made from fine string

You can vary the number of masts and sails you make to suit the piece of wood.

Caveman's cart
You can use your cart to display some of your nature treasures. Then why not try making little cavemen out of sticks and string, to pull the cart along?

Yard-arm made from a short stick

Fine thread joints

Jaunty clipper
This driftwood boat would look good on show in your room or decorating the bathroom.

Feather shaft for a bowsprit

Yellow and green pattern

Old piece of rope for the waves

SPINNING WINDMILLS

Try making these colourful paper windmills. Big windmills catch the wind in their sails to grind corn into flour, to pump water, or even to produce electricity, but these little windmills are just for fun. See how fast you can make them spin by blowing on their sails. When the weather is fine, take them outside to spin round in the wind.

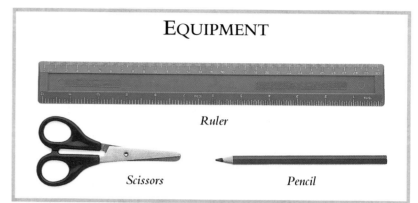

EQUIPMENT

Ruler

Scissors

Pencil

You will need

Pins with a large head

Small beads

Pencils with a rubber on the end

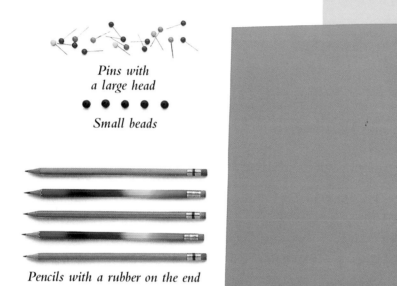

Sheets of coloured paper

What to do

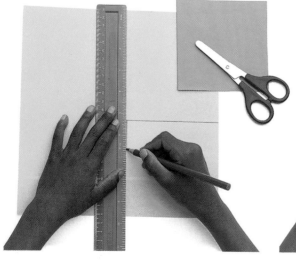

1 Using the ruler, measure out and draw two squares the same size on two different-coloured pieces of paper (see page 60). Cut out the squares.

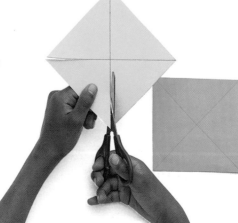

2 Using the ruler again, draw two diagonal lines across each square so they cross in the middle. Cut only two thirds of the way along each line.

3 Hold the squares of paper together. Bend the paper back along each cut line into the centre, as shown, and hold the corners down.

Make sure the sharp end of the pin doesn't stick out of the rubber.

Bead

Big windmill with red and yellow sails

Blue pin

Red pin

Rainbow pencil handle

Blue and yellow sails

Green and yellow sails

Make sure that the point of your pencil isn't sharp.

Green pin

4 Push a pin through all the corners of the paper, then through a bead and into the rubber at the end of a pencil.

5 Blow on the windmill to make it spin. Does it work best if you blow from the side or the front?

Test of strength
Use a windmill to test how windy it is. The faster the sails of your windmill turn, the stronger the wind is.

Host of windmills

Here are all the finished windmills. You can make windmills with bigger or smaller sails by using different sized squares of paper. If the paper is very thick you will only need one square of paper.

Orange pencil handle

FINGER PUPPETS

You can make a cheerful handful of finger puppets using the template shown on page 63. Make the puppets from brightly-coloured felt, or from any scraps of fabric or paper you can find at home. Try the animal puppets shown here, or invent some of your own.

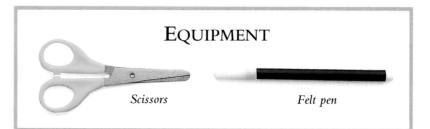

EQUIPMENT

Scissors

Felt pen

You will need

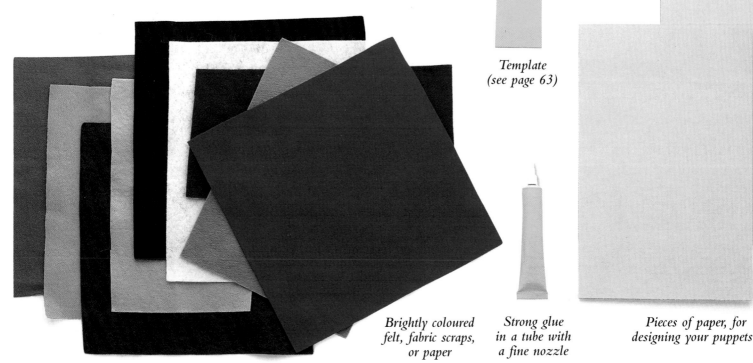

Template (see page 63)

Brightly coloured felt, fabric scraps, or paper

Strong glue in a tube with a fine nozzle

Pieces of paper, for designing your puppets

What to do

1 Draw your designs for puppets on paper before you make them. Look at pictures of animals or people to get some ideas, then simplify them.

2 Lay the body template on a piece of felt and draw around it twice. Draw the puppet features on other pieces of felt. Cut out the body pieces.

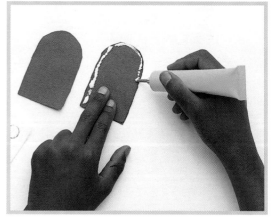

3 Spread a fine line of glue around the curved edge of one piece of the body, leaving the bottom edge free. Press the two body pieces together.

Cheerful puppets

You could make a whole troupe of smiling animals like these, or a collection of characters from fairy tales. Your puppets will work best if they are simple and brightly coloured. Why not make up a play for the puppets with a friend!

Put the puppet on your index finger.

4 Now carefully cut out the puppet's features that you drew on the other pieces of felt. Remember to cut out two arms, two legs, etc.

5 Arrange the cut-out features on the body to see how they look. If any part doesn't look quite right, try making another version of it.

6 First glue the legs and arms (or wings and paws) to the back of the body. Then glue the rest of the animal's features on to the front.

Mouse

Owl

Lion

Panda

Cockerel

Frog

Parrot

Pig

Moving the puppets

Make the puppets look as though they are talking by moving your fingers.

Curl your other fingers and thumb away from the puppet.

The paws are glued to inside the of the puppet's body.

45

KALEIDOSCOPE

A kaleidoscope is a very clever toy – hold it to your eye, turn it round, and watch an unending display of patterns. You will need shiny mirror board, which you buy at an art shop, or make from aluminium foil glued on card. The kaleidoscope works best if the coloured plastic pieces are thicker than paper.

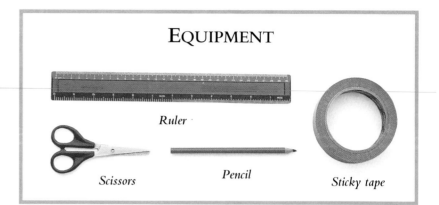

EQUIPMENT

Ruler

Scissors

Pencil

Sticky tape

You will need

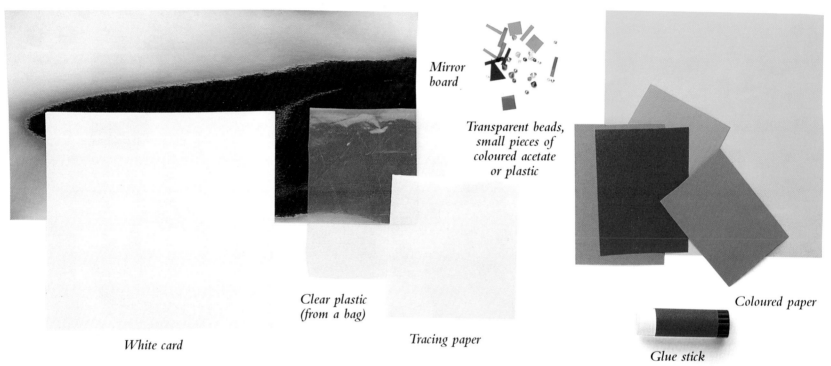

Mirror board

Transparent beads, small pieces of coloured acetate or plastic

Coloured paper

Clear plastic (from a bag)

Tracing paper

Glue stick

White card

What to do

1 Cut out a piece of mirror board 12 cm by 20 cm. Measure out and score two lines along it lengthways 4 cm apart.

2 Fold the board along the lines, so the mirror is inside. Tape the two edges together. Then tape a piece of clear plastic over one end of the tube.

3 Cut a piece of mirror board 12.5 cm by 3 cm. Tape it round the tube, so that it sticks out over the plastic-covered end, as shown.

What to do (continued)

4 Hold the tube upright with the short piece of tube you have added at the top. Drop small pieces of coloured plastic and beads into it.

5 Cut out a triangular piece of tracing paper. Lay it flat over the top of the tube. Fold the edges over the tube and tape them down.

6 Cut out a piece of coloured paper 12.5 cm by 20 cm. Glue it round the tube, as shown, then decorate it with coloured paper shapes.

Pocket rainbows

Here is the finished kaleidoscope, decorated with colourful paper rectangles and squares. To make it work, face a window or a bright light and close one eye. Hold the open end of the tube up to your other eye, look into the tube, and slowly turn the kaleidoscope round. Here are the sorts of patterns you may see.

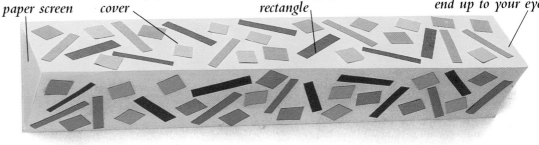

Tracing paper screen   *Yellow paper cover*   *Coloured paper rectangle*   *Hold the open end up to your eye*

As you turn the kaleidoscope round in your hands, the pattern will change before your eyes.

Green plastic bead   *Green acetate strip*   *Blue acetate strip*

Red acetate triangle   *Blue plastic bead*

47

JUNK MODELS

You do not need expensive materials or kits to make exciting models. Here you can learn how to make toy binoculars, a truck, a robot, and an impressive castle – all from everyday rubbish that you would normally just throw away. Turn the page to find out how to put the finishing touches to the models.

Turn the page to find out how to put the finishing touches to the models.

EQUIPMENT

Thick paintbrush

Scissors

Spatula

Jar of water

Sticky tape

Thin paintbrush

You will need

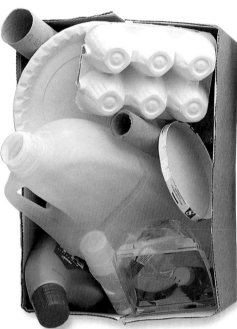

Empty cartons, tubes, and packets

Cardboard boxes

Cardboard toilet roll tubes

PVA glue

Long cardboard rolls

Corrugated card from old boxes

Paper clips

Paper fasteners

Safety pins

Poster paints

Plastic drinking straws

Clear varnish

Old aluminium foil

Plastic sweet containers

Plastic bottle tops

String

Making binoculars

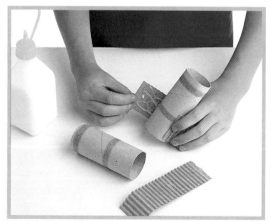

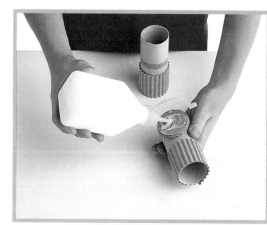

1 Cut two strips of corrugated card 5 cm wide and long enough to wrap round a toilet roll tube. Glue one round the end of each tube.

2 Draw round a tube four times on corrugated card and cut out the four circles. Glue them together between the two tubes, as shown.

3 Ask an adult to make a hole in each tube. Thread a piece of string through the holes, and tie a knot in each end, as shown.

Making the truck

1 Find two boxes and a lid like these. Draw windows on the front and sides of the larger box and cut them out. This will be the cab of the truck.

2 Glue the box lid and the two boxes together on top of a piece of card. Glue three small tubes underneath the truck for the wheels.

3 Push plastic bottle tops into the ends of the tubes to complete the wheels. Then paint the truck with brightly coloured poster paints.

Making the castle

1 Find a large square box for the base of the castle. Cut four strips of card, each the same length as a side of the box. Cut battlements along them.

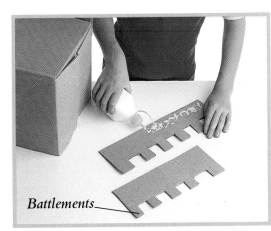

Battlements

2 Spread glue along the base of each strip of battlements and glue them around the base of the box, as shown, so that the battlements stick up.

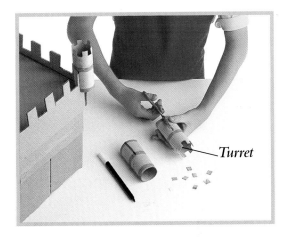

Turret

3 For turrets, cut battlements at the tops of four small tubes. Cut two slits in each tube and slot them on to the four corners of the castle.

4 Use a long tube for a tall tower. Cut battlements in a strip of paper and glue it around the top. Then glue on a cone of paper for the roof.

5 Make small buildings for the castle from smaller boxes. Use corrugated card to make roofs, windows, and doors. Then paint the buildings.

6 Glue all the bits of the castle together. Paint it, adding crosses for windows. Make flags from folded paper triangles and tape them to straws.

CARDBOARD CREATIONS

Making the robot

Here are some of the models you can create. The truck and binoculars only take an hour or so to make. The robot takes a bit longer, and the castle at least an afternoon. The models you make will look different, depending on the boxes and bits of junk you use. Have fun experimenting!

1 Attach small tube arms to the box body with paper fasteners. Ask an adult to make a hole first, then push the fasteners through, and fold open the legs.

2 Glue the rest of the boxes together as shown. Use two small tubes for the legs and small boxes for the head, feet, and chest.

3 Paint the robot and leave it to dry. Then coat with clear varnish. When the varnish is dry, add details for the face, hands, uniform, and instrument panel.

Plastic lid for a hat

Pieces of egg box covered in foil for ears

Sweet case for a mask

Safety pin mouth

Small box for the head

Foil-covered bottle tops for epaulets

Paper clips for the instrument panel

Small cardboard tube arm

Foil-covered bottle top for a hand

Gold press-studs for buttons

Robot captain
The basic robot is made up of one large box and four smaller boxes, with cardboard tubes for arms and legs. Paint your robot a bright colour, then add shiny details with paper clips, press-studs and foil-covered bottle tops.

Cardboard tubes for legs

Small boxes for feet

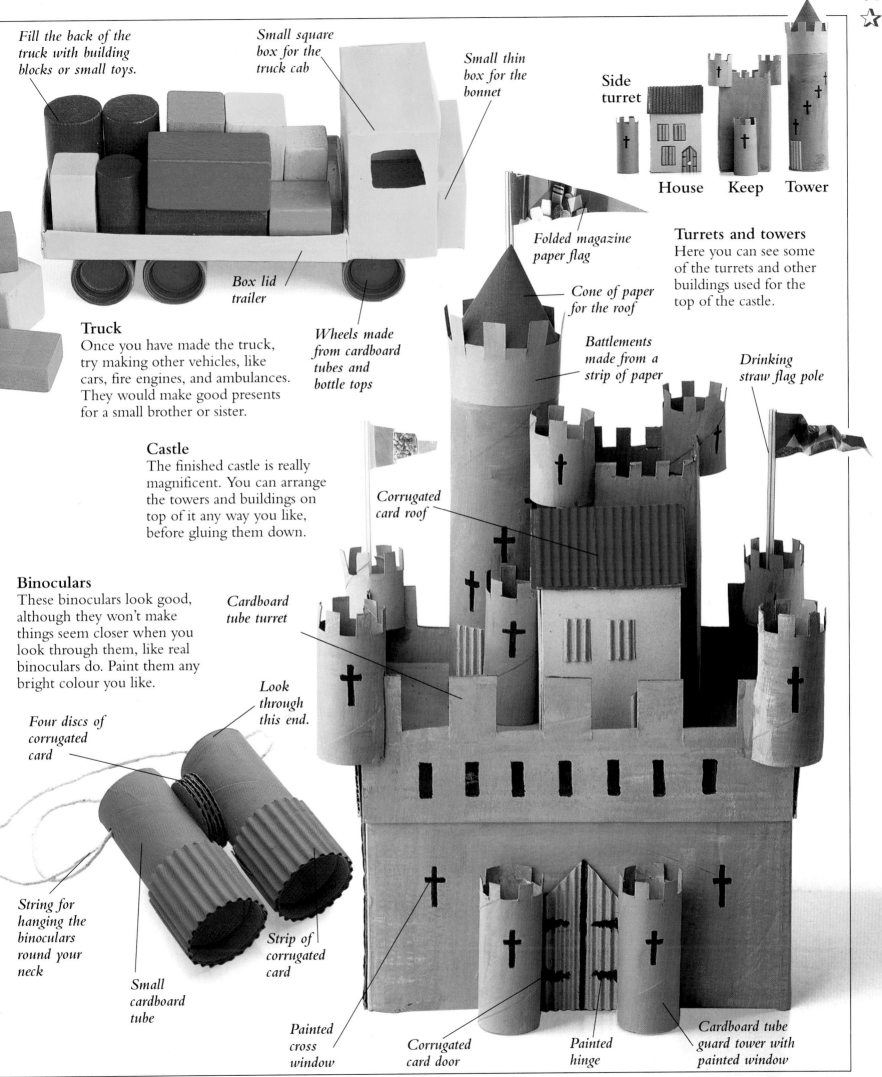

Fill the back of the truck with building blocks or small toys.

Small square box for the truck cab

Small thin box for the bonnet

Side turret

House   Keep   Tower

Turrets and towers
Here you can see some of the turrets and other buildings used for the top of the castle.

Folded magazine paper flag

Cone of paper for the roof

Box lid trailer

Truck
Once you have made the truck, try making other vehicles, like cars, fire engines, and ambulances. They would make good presents for a small brother or sister.

Wheels made from cardboard tubes and bottle tops

Battlements made from a strip of paper

Drinking straw flag pole

Castle
The finished castle is really magnificent. You can arrange the towers and buildings on top of it any way you like, before gluing them down.

Corrugated card roof

Binoculars
These binoculars look good, although they won't make things seem closer when you look through them, like real binoculars do. Paint them any bright colour you like.

Cardboard tube turret

Look through this end.

Four discs of corrugated card

String for hanging the binoculars round your neck

Small cardboard tube

Strip of corrugated card

Painted cross window

Corrugated card door

Painted hinge

Cardboard tube guard tower with painted window

SHADOW PUPPETS

Putting on a shadow play with your friends
is a great way to spend a rainy afternoon.
Here you can find out how to make brightly
coloured shadow puppets with moving joints.
Turn the page to see how to make the
shadow theatre and to find out how to
work the puppets and put on a show.

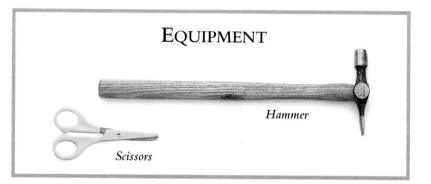

EQUIPMENT

Hammer

Scissors

You will need

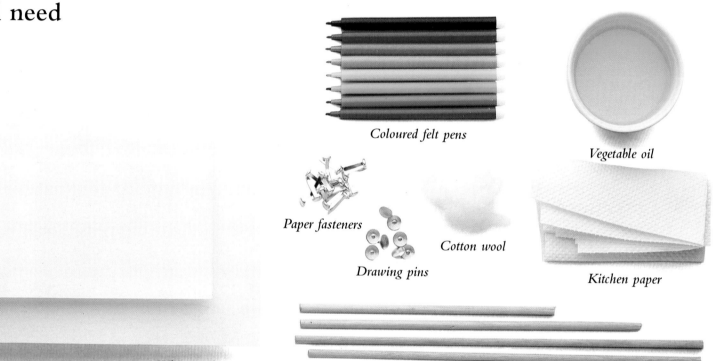

Coloured felt pens

Vegetable oil

Paper fasteners

Cotton wool

Drawing pins

Kitchen paper

White card

2 or 3 pieces of dowelling about 30 cm long for each puppet

Making a puppet

1 Draw the puppet you want to
make on white card with a black
felt pen. Keep the shape simple and
add details such as stripes or spots.

2 Colour in the puppet with felt
pens. The brighter the colours,
the better the puppet will look in the
theatre. Then cut it out carefully.

3 Next, cut off any part of the
puppet that you want to be able
to move. This puppet will have a
neck that can move up and down.

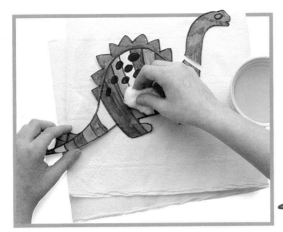

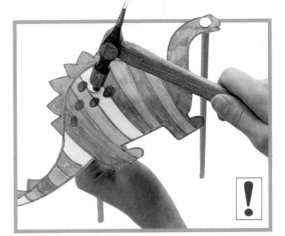

4 Lay the puppet on some kitchen paper and dab it all over with cotton wool soaked in vegetable oil. Do this to both sides of each puppet.

5 Make holes with a drawing pin in the parts of the puppet you want to join. Push a paper fastener through each hole, and fold the legs open.

6 Then ask an adult to join a dowel stick to both parts of the puppet, by hammering a drawing pin into the end of a stick, as shown.

Puppet world

Here are some ideas for shadow puppets and scenery for the theatre. Copy these, or make puppets of characters from your favourite stories.

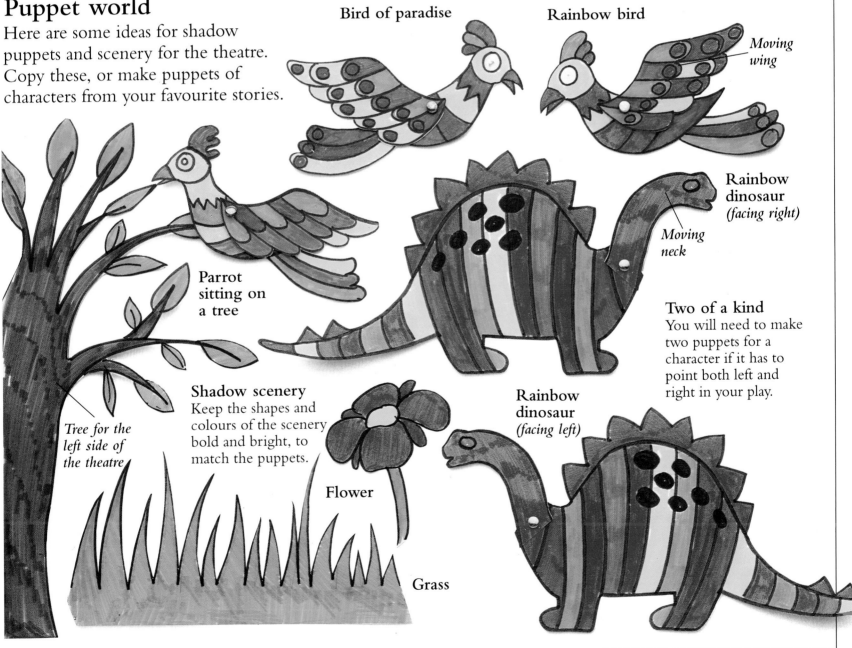

Bird of paradise

Rainbow bird

Moving wing

Parrot sitting on a tree

Tree for the left side of the theatre

Shadow scenery
Keep the shapes and colours of the scenery bold and bright, to match the puppets.

Flower

Grass

Rainbow dinosaur *(facing right)*

Moving neck

Two of a kind
You will need to make two puppets for a character if it has to point both left and right in your play.

Rainbow dinosaur *(facing left)*

WORLD IN A THEATRE

To bring the puppets to life, stand the theatre on a table near a bright light, such as a lamp, so that light shines in through the back of the box, and on to the puppets and the screen. Make up a simple story script, and then you are ready to rehearse. You will need to ask a friend to help you, as two hands are needed to work each puppet.

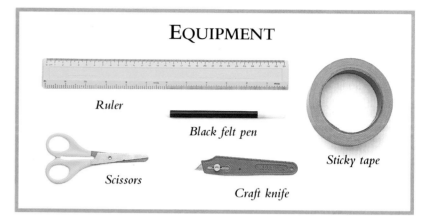

EQUIPMENT

Ruler

Black felt pen

Sticky tape

Scissors

Craft knife

You will need

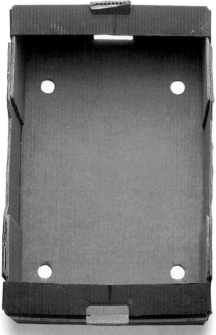

A strong, rectangular cardboard box

Coloured paper for decorating the theatre

Glue stick

Tracing paper or greaseproof paper

Making the theatre

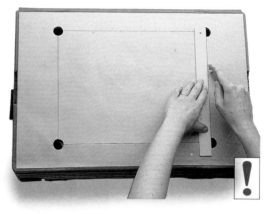

1 Measure and draw a rectangle on the bottom of the cardboard box, as shown. Then ask an adult to cut it out of the box with a craft knife.

3 Tape the pieces of scenery you have made, such as trees, flowers, and grass, coloured-side down on to the paper screen inside the box.

2 Cut out a rectangle of tracing paper a little bigger than the hole in the box. Tape the sides of the paper down over the hole, inside the box.

4 Turn the box over. Cut out shapes from coloured paper and glue them round the edge of the screen, to make the box look like a real theatre.

Make the bird fly by moving its wing up and down.

Slide the puppet across the screen as you move its wing.

Hold one puppet stick in each hand.

Moving puppets

You will need both hands to make each puppet move, one for each stick. To bring a puppet to life, slide it along the back of the screen, while moving the sticks.

Behind the scenes
When you are ready to perform your play, stand to one side, behind the screen.

Move your arm up and down to move the dinosaur's head.

Be careful not to block out the light from your light source.

Decorate the front of the theatre with coloured paper shapes.

Rainbow dinosaur

Stick the scenery to the sides of the theatre.

RAGGY DOLLS

Here and overleaf are some wonderful things to sew – teddies, little cats and bears, pretty hearts, a rag doll, and a rabbit. You can make all of them using leftover pieces of fabric you have at home. You will find the templates on pages 62 and 63, and help with easy sewing stitches on page 61.

You will find the templates on pages 62 and 63, and help with easy sewing stitches on page 61.

EQUIPMENT

Pencil

Needle

Pins

Safety pin

Scissors

Pinking shears

You will need

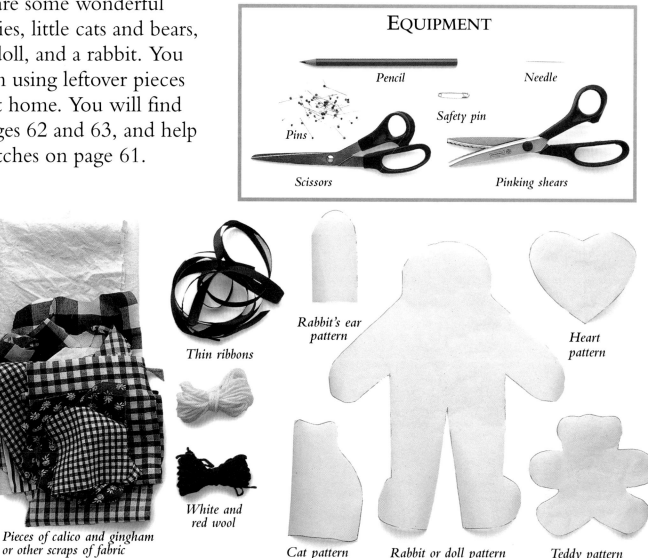

Kapok or other soft stuffing

Reels of thread

Pieces of calico and gingham or other scraps of fabric

Thin ribbons

White and red wool

Rabbit's ear pattern

Heart pattern

Cat pattern

Rabbit or doll pattern

Teddy pattern

(See pages 62 and 63 for all the templates)

Making the toys

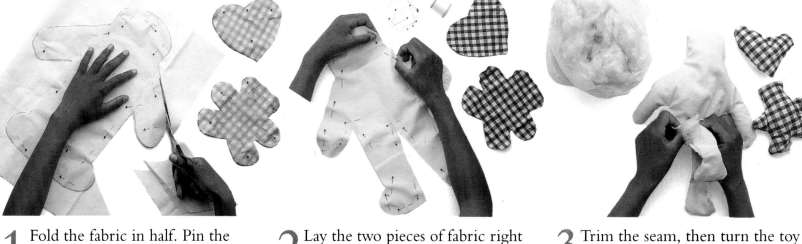

1 Fold the fabric in half. Pin the pattern to the folded fabric and cut it out, as shown, to give you two pieces. Then unpin the pattern.

2 Lay the two pieces of fabric right sides together. Pin and then sew★ them together, leaving a gap 5 cm wide at the end of the seam.

3 Trim the seam, then turn the toy inside out. Use a pencil to push out any narrow points. Then push some stuffing into the toy.

★ *Use running stitch for all seams, as shown on page 61.*

Finishing the rabbit

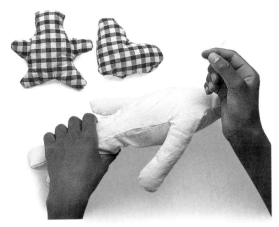

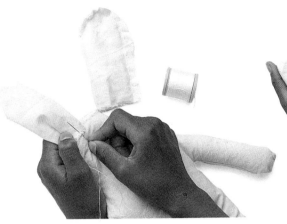

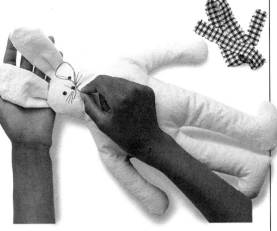

4 Use a pencil to push stuffing into any small corners. When the toy seems fat enough, sew up the gap in the seam, using overstitch.

1 Fold the rabbit ears in half and sew★ round the outer edges. Turn them inside out. Sew them to the top of the rabbit's head using overstitch.

2 Sew eyes, a nose, a mouth, and whiskers on the rabbit's face using backstitch. Cut a strip of fabric and tie it on like a bow tie.

Finishing the doll

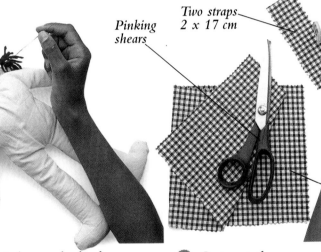

Long strands of red wool

White wool

Pinking shears

Two straps 2 x 17 cm

Bib 5 x 8 cm

Apron skirt 30 x 18 cm

1 Tie white wool round the doll's neck. Sew red wool to her head for hair. Sew two ribbons to her face. Tie them in bows round her hair.

2 Plait the hair beneath the bows and tie each plait with red wool. Then sew two eyes and a mouth on to the doll's face, using backstitch.

3 Cut out the apron pieces with shears. Fold the straps in half and overstitch them to the bib. Put the bib on the doll so the straps cross at the back.

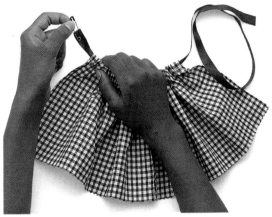

Trim off the ends of the ribbon.

Tie the apron round the doll.

4 Cut a 30 cm length of ribbon. Fold the top of the apron over by 1 cm and pin it down. Sew★ along the cut edge, to make a casing.

5 Fasten a safety pin to one end of the ribbon and thread the ribbon though the casing. Then gather the skirt evenly along the ribbon.

DOLLS AND TEDDIES

Add bows and ribbons to your toys to give them a finishing touch. You can make them in matching fabrics as we have done here, or use any scraps you find at home. All of them would make good presents.

Dancing bears
Make three little bears. Tie bows round their necks and stitch them together at the paws. Then sew ribbons at each end of the row of bears. These make an ideal decoration for a baby's pram or cot.

Red wool hair tied into plaits.

Embroidered face

Blue ribbon bow

Sew a red ribbon bow around each teddy's neck.

Gingham apron

Blue ribbon bow

Martha doll
Martha is made of white calico and has a checked apron, to give her an American prairies look.

Soft hearts cushion
Make four stuffed hearts in different fabrics that go well together. Sew them together to make a flower shape and stitch a bow in the centre.

Red stripy
fabric

Ribbons for tying
up the bears

Broad ribbon
loop for hanging
up the hearts

Embroidered
face and
whiskers

Gingham
bow tie

Red bow of
thin ribbon

White rabbit
The rabbit is made from the
same pattern as Martha
doll, only he has floppy
ears as well. Tie a
jaunty bow tie round
his neck. Make him
a posy of dried
flowers and sew
them on the
inside of
one paw.

Tie a red bow
around the
cat's neck to
give it a little
more shape.

Row of
hearts
Make four
stuffed hearts.
Sew a loop at
the top of a
broad ribbon,
then sew the
hearts beneath it.

Little cat
Make the little cat from simple checked
fabric and tie a bow round its neck.

HANDY HINTS

This picture guide shows you all the useful craft and sewing skills that you need to make the projects in this book.

Scoring a fold

Drawing a circle

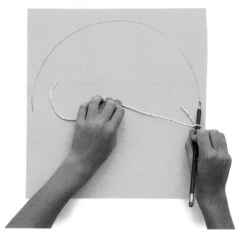

1 To make a sharp fold in card you must score the fold-line first. Hold the ruler along the fold-line and run the tip of your scissors along the line.

2 Be careful not to cut right through the card! Gently smooth the fold down flat along the scored line. The card should fold over easily.

Tie a pencil to a piece of string. Hold the string where you want the centre of the circle to be. Move the pencil around it, keeping the string taut.

Drawing a square

1 Starting from one corner of a piece of paper, measure along one edge and draw a dot. Then draw another dot the same distance along the other edge.

2 Imagine or draw a diagonal line between the two dots and fold the paper along it. Draw a dot at the folded corner of the paper, as shown.

3 Open out the paper and join the centre dot to the two dots at the edges of the paper. Cut along these two lines, to make a perfect square.

Transferring a template

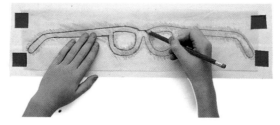

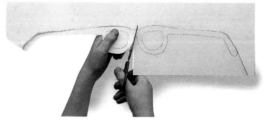

1 Trace the template from the outline on pages 62 and 63. Turn the tracing paper over and scribble all over the back of it, as shown.

2 Turn the tracing paper over and tape it on to a piece of card, to hold it steady. Then carefully draw over the lines of the tracing.

3 Remove the tracing paper. The tracing will have transferred on to the card below. Cut out the shape along the lines of the tracing.

Using a sewing pattern

The templates for all the sewing projects are on pages 62-63. To make a pattern, trace the template you need on to a piece of tracing paper, and cut it out. Then follow steps 1 and 2 to cut out the fabric pieces. When cutting out two pieces from a pattern, fold the fabric in half, right sides together, with its pattern running straight up and down.

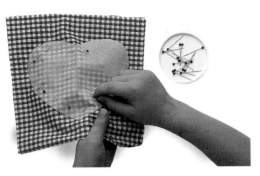

1 Pin the pattern piece to the fabric, making sure that the pattern is lying straight along the fabric pattern, as shown.

2 Cut around the edge of the pattern piece. Turn the fabric as you cut, so that the scissors are always pointing away from you.

Trimming a seam

Trimming off the spare fabric around a seam makes the finished seam look neat. Cut halfway between the seam line and the edge, as shown.

Overstitch

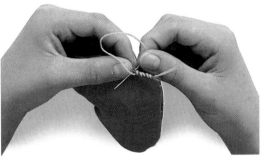

1 Fold in the edges of the fabric. Tie a knot in one end of the thread★, then push the needle through both folded edges from back to front.

2 Take the needle round to the back again and repeat the stitch until the seam is finished.

Running stitch

Tie a knot in the end of the thread★, and push the needle through both pieces of fabric then back through to the front, as shown in step 1. Then pull the thread and the needle out through the fabric (step 2). Repeat steps 1 and 2, until you have finished the seam.

Backstitch

Tie a knot in the thread★. Make the first stitch as for running stitch. Then put the needle through the hole at the end of the first stitch and up again a little way in front of the stitch you have just made, as shown in step 1. Repeat steps 1 and 2, until you have finished the seam.

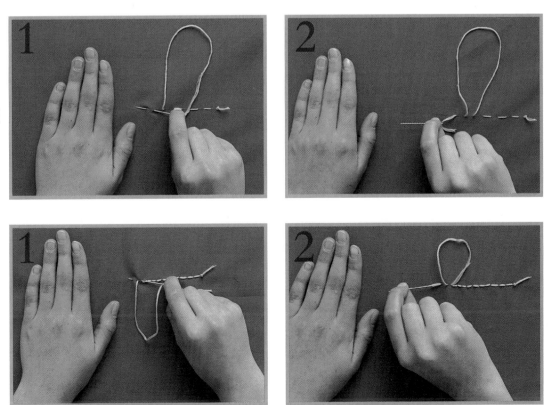

★For a strong seam, use a double thickness of ordinary sewing thread.

TEMPLATES

Here are the templates for the soft toys on pages 58-59, the disguises on pages 12-13, and the puppets on page 44-45. You can find out how to make the templates and patterns on pages 60 and 61. Read the labels around the template you need before you start to make it.

Using a pattern
Ask an adult to help you line up the top and bottom of the pattern with the grain of the fabric before pinning them both together.

Cutting line

Cutting line

Top

White rabbit's ears
Make a tracing paper pattern, as shown on page 61, then cut out two ears. Fold each ear in half along the dotted line and sew along the open sides, about 1 cm in from the cut edge.

Fold line

Bottom

Top

Top

Top

Fold line

Cutting line

Little cat
Make a tracing paper pattern, as shown on page 61. Fold a piece of fabric in half, right sides together, and pin the pattern to the fabric so that the dotted line lies along the fold. Cut the fabric out and then sew the open sides together, about 1 cm in from the cut edge.

Bottom

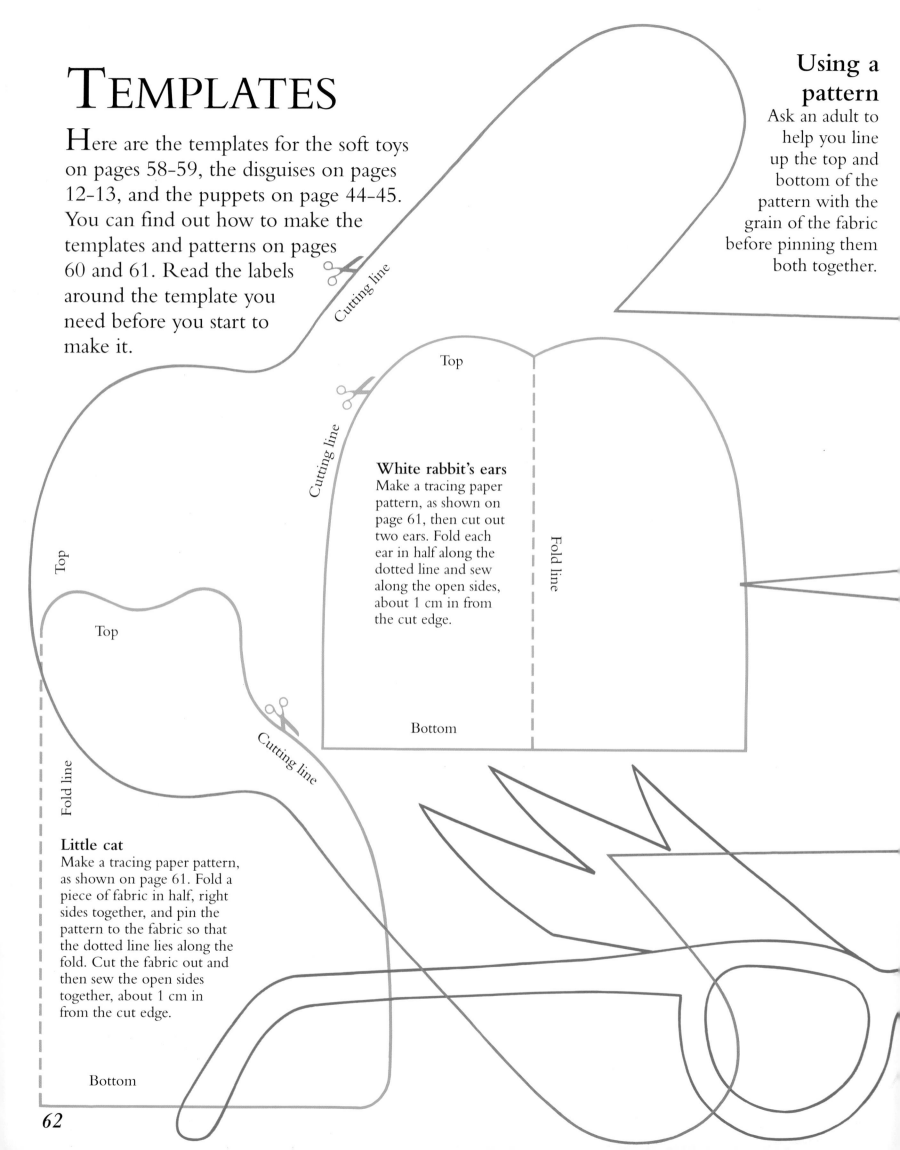

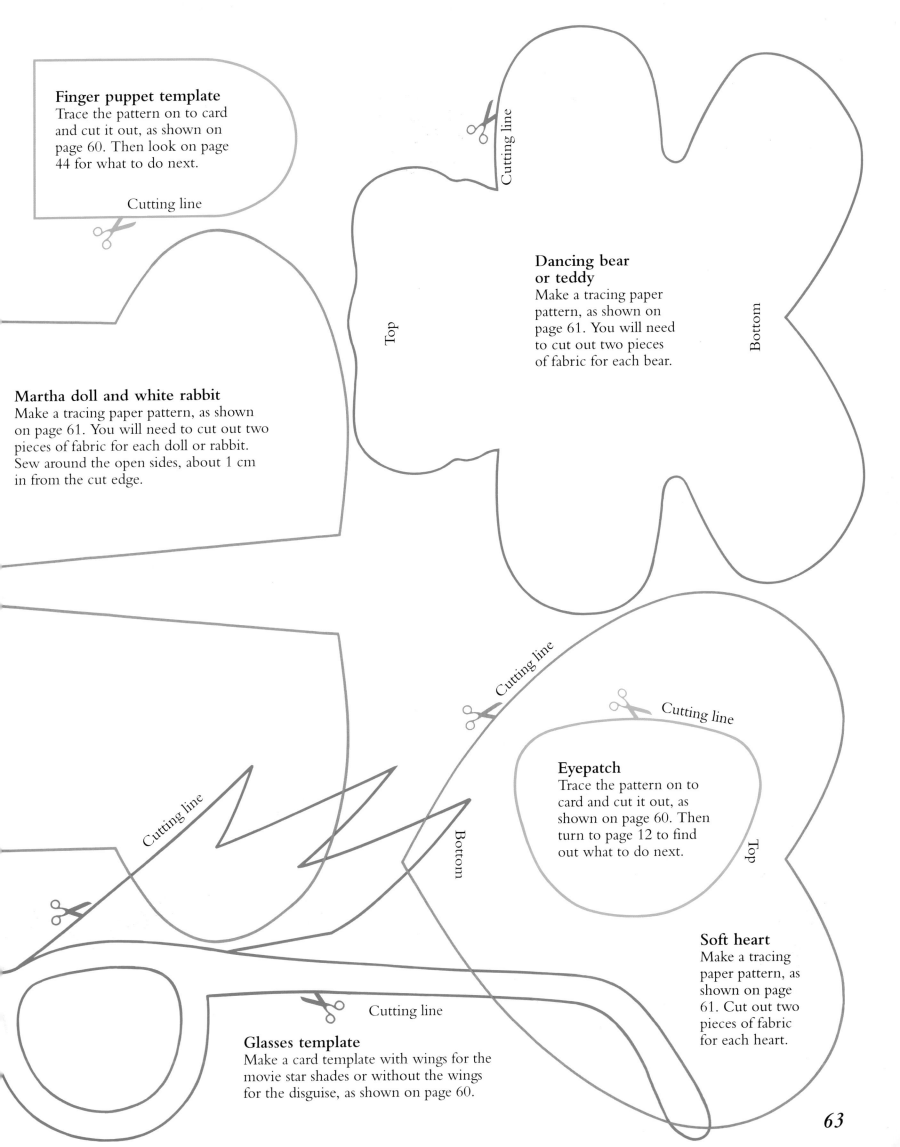

Finger puppet template
Trace the pattern on to card and cut it out, as shown on page 60. Then look on page 44 for what to do next.

Cutting line

Cutting line

Dancing bear or teddy
Make a tracing paper pattern, as shown on page 61. You will need to cut out two pieces of fabric for each bear.

Top

Bottom

Martha doll and white rabbit
Make a tracing paper pattern, as shown on page 61. You will need to cut out two pieces of fabric for each doll or rabbit. Sew around the open sides, about 1 cm in from the cut edge.

Cutting line

Cutting line

Cutting line

Bottom

Eyepatch
Trace the pattern on to card and cut it out, as shown on page 60. Then turn to page 12 to find out what to do next.

Top

Soft heart
Make a tracing paper pattern, as shown on page 61. Cut out two pieces of fabric for each heart.

Cutting line

Glasses template
Make a card template with wings for the movie star shades or without the wings for the disguise, as shown on page 60.

INDEX